ethics will be violated if any nation proceeds with irresponsible investigations of other planets, in our own or other solar systems. A terrestrial rocket could carry earthly organisms which would contaminate and interfere with biological development.

The author closes on a note of optimism: In attempts to reach the moon first, there seems to be a beginning toward making the rivalry between the United States and the USSR a constructive one. With concentration on exploration there must of necessity be less stress on destructive rivalries. *8 pages photographs.*

I. The Thor Able rocket combination at Cape Canaveral before the launching of the space probe Pioneer V. (*By kind permission of Space Technology Laboratories, Los Angeles.*)

THE
EXPLORATION
OF
OUTER SPACE

SIR BERNARD LOVELL

HARPER & ROW, PUBLISHERS
NEW YORK AND EVANSTON

Library of Congress Catalog Card Number: 62-14566

CONTENTS

NOTE: Throughout this book the word "billion" means the English billion, namely, one million million. References to "trillion" indicate the figure one, followed by eighteen zeros.

ILLUSTRATIONS

PLATES

I The Thor Able rocket combination at Cape Canaveral before the launching of the space probe Pioneer V. (*By kind permission of Space Technology Laboratories, Los Angeles*) *frontispiece*

The following plates will be found in a group after page 40.

II The space probe Pioneer V launched on 11 March 1960. (*By kind permission of Space Technology Laboratories, Los Angeles*)

III The 250-ft. radio telescope at Jodrell Bank photographed when a helicopter was removing from the base of the aerial mast inside the bowl the transmitter which was used to command the Pioneer V space probe. (*By kind permission of the* Daily Mail)

IV A large group of sunspots photographed on 17 May 1951. (*By courtesy of the Mount Wilson and Palomar Observatories*)

V The relation between red-shift and distance for extra-galactic nebulae. (*By courtesy of the Mount Wilson and Palomar Observatories*)

VI The 200-inch Hale telescope on Mount Palomar showing the observer in the prime focus cage and the reflecting surface of the 200-inch mirror. (*By courtesy of the Mount Wilson and Palomar Observatories*)

VII The Great Spiral Nebula in Andromeda (M31) photographed with the 48-inch Schmidt camera on Mount Palomar. (*By courtesy of the Mount Wilson and Palomar Observatories*)

VIII (*a*) The Lagoon Nebula (M8) in Sagittarius. (*By courtesy of the Mount Wilson and Palomar Observatories*)

(*b*) The Crab Nebula—the remains of a supernova explosion which was observed by Chinese astronomers in 1054. (*By courtesy of the Mount Wilson and Palomar Observatories*)

IX A group of four nebulae in the constellation Leo photographed by the 200-inch Palomar telescope. (*By courtesy of the Mount Wilson and Palomar Observatories*)

iv

TEXT FIGURES

PREFACE

This book is based on the Gregynog Lectures which I gave in October 1961 in the University of Wales at Aberystwyth under the title of *The Exploration of Outer Space*. The first four chapters are equivalent to the four lectures which were delivered on successive evenings to an audience predominantly consisting of undergraduates. The hall was not adequate to contain all those who attended the lectures and the intense interest of this packed audience under conditions which must have been extremely uncomfortable was, in itself, an inspiration.

The fifth chapter of this book is not based on any specific part of the Gregynog Lectures. During the summer of 1961 I became increasingly obsessed with the dangers of certain developments in space research, and this essay on 'Ethics and the Cosmos' was written before the Gregynog Lectures and has appeared in modified form in the *Sunday Times* and in the *New York Times*. It seemed appropriate to the general subject matter of the book and appears here in its full and original version.

It is not uncommon for lectures to be published, often in the journals of learned societies and sometimes in book form. Frequently the question of publication may be a matter to be decided by the lecturer, but in some cases it may be a condition that the lecture should be published. The Greynog Lecturer has such an obligation. Some lecturers prepare a script in detail before they lecture and may even read their lecture from it. For them, publication is no burden. I envy them, for I find a script or even extensive notes a burden, and as with many other lectures I found myself with nothing but slides on the eve of the Gregynog Lectures. It was at this point that someone suggested the solution of the tape recorder, and since the recordings of moon echoes and moon probe signals were to be played in one of the lectures there seemed no reason why the spoken word should not be recorded on tape and transcribed directly into book form.

Many years ago after speaking at a scientific meeting and having failed to produce a manuscript, I was asked to approve for publication the copy of my speech made by a stenographer. This typed record was so incoherent—either with sentences which were incomplete, or with sentences begun and then restarted on a different line of thought—that it seemed impossible that it could bear much relation to what I said and it was natural to assume that the stenographer was at fault. Nevertheless in subsequent years, when tape recordings were able to provide a check on secretarial transcriptions, I realized with some dismay that the things I said were not in the precise form which they might have been had they been read from a manuscript—particularly when slides or illustrations were used in the exposition.

Even so, I prefer to see my audience. Unless the circumstances are unusual, or the subject is remote from my daily work, I resent the tie of the manuscript—because I want to study the people to whom I am talking and deal with the subject according to their reactions. In the case of these lectures the spoken word has required a good deal of changing before being ready for publication.

I am extremely grateful to Professor Cocconi of Cornell University for his permission to reprint the letter which he wrote to me in the summer of 1959 and which is published here in the Appendix. I am also indebted to Mr. R. G. Lascelles for his invaluable assistance with the illustrations and to Miss Anthea Hollinshead who had the unenviable task of transcribing the Gregynog Lectures from tape to type and of further interpreting the corrected typescript.

JODRELL BANK   A. C. B. LOVELL
JULY 1962

I
THE TECHNIQUES OF INVESTIGATION

THE NATURE OF THE UNIVERSE

M AN's view of the universe has been enormously expanded during the decades since the close of the second world war, primarily because of the new techniques of radio astronomy and the space probe. It was, however, the introduction of the great optical telescopes which led to the major revolution in our ideas about the size and organization of the cosmos. Until twenty-five or thirty years ago we still believed that the system of stars visible in the sky on any clear night, and known as the Milky Way, was confined in space and itself represented the totality of the universe. Even so short a time ago we believed that the sun, the earth, and the attendant planets were situated at the centre of this system of stars, and that the sun was a typical star and seemed bright because it was close to us. The stars appeared faint, not because they were small and insignificant, but because they were at great distances. Nevertheless we believed that we were privileged to be situated in the centre of this assembly. It was estimated that there were many thousands of millions of stars in this Milky Way system and they were believed to be distributed in an approximately spherical enclosure of a size such that it would take a ray of light travelling 186,000 miles a second a few thousand years to traverse it. These ideas have been changed completely.

The investigations which were carried out by the American astronomers in the few years after 1920 following the opening of the 100-inch telescope on Mount Wilson showed that this egocentric view was wrong; that, in fact, the stars of the Milky Way were arranged in a disc of extent such that a ray of light would take a hundred thousand years to traverse the distance separating the extremities of the stars, and that the system was asymmetrical. If one could remove oneself from the Milky Way system and look back on it through a large telescope then the stars would appear to be arranged in a flattened disc with the stars concentrated in spirals radiating from the central hub like a gaint octopus. It was realized too that the sun, far from being at the centre of this disc of stars, was situated in an unfavourable position somewhere near the edge of the disc.

We know that this Milky Way system or local galaxy contains about one hundred thousand million stars. The earth is a planet of the sun's family, 93 million miles away. The most distant planet in our solar system, Pluto, is a few thousand million miles distant, so far away that the light from the sun takes about $6\frac{1}{2}$ hours on its journey towards the planet Pluto. These distances, which are still just conceivable in terrestrial terms, are minute compared with the distance which separates our solar family from the nearest star in space. In order to describe these distances it is convenient to use the expression known as the 'light year', which is the distance which a ray of light travels during the course of a year. The speed of light is 186,000 miles per second; the light from the sun takes 8 minutes on its journey, therefore the sun is at a distance of 8 light minutes. The light from Pluto takes $6\frac{1}{2}$ hours on its journey to earth so Pluto is $6\frac{1}{2}$ light hours away. On the other hand the nearest star is enormously more distant, so far away that the light from it takes $4\frac{1}{2}$ years on its journey.

It is important to realize that our knowledge in astronomy is almost entirely of time past. We have no knowledge whatsoever of time present. Our knowledge of the sun is 8 minutes old, our knowledge of the nearest star is $4\frac{1}{2}$ years out of date, and our knowledge of some of the stars which we see in the Milky Way may be a hundred thousand years out of date because the light from these stars has taken a hundred thousand years on its journey through space towards us. The presence in the sky of faint nebulous patches had been known for a very long time and in fact Herschel speculated in the nineteenth century that these nebulae might indeed be other systems of stars outside our Milky Way system; but it was not until the 100-inch telescope on Mount Wilson came into use that Hubble was able to show that this was indeed the case. There is such a nebulous object, visible to the naked eye under good conditions, in the constellation of Andromeda. We know that this object is not a nebulous region of gas amongst the stars of the Milky Way but another great system of stars so far away that the light from it has taken 2 million years on its journey towards us. This M31 nebula in Andromeda is outside our own galaxy or Milky Way system, 2 million light years distant. In many respects it seems that our own Milky Way system is very similar to this spiral galaxy in

◄─────── 100,000 LIGHT YEARS ───────►

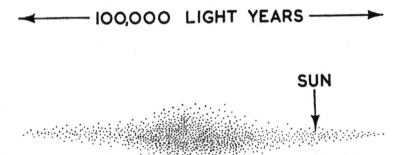

Fig. 1. The position of the Sun in the plane of the Milky Way.

Andromeda, not only in the spiral arrangement of the stars but also in size and stellar content. As seen through the great optical telescopes, space appears to be populated everywhere with these galaxies of stars. Extragalactic nebulae are scattered to such great distances that at the limit of our penetration the light from the galaxies has been thousands of millions of years on its journey through space towards us. Within this observable region of the cosmos there must be trillions of galaxies of stars which are bright enough to be recorded on the photographic plate of the 200-inch Palomar telescope.

These tremendous changes in our view of space have been brought about largely because of the introduction of the big optical telescope. It is over 300 years since Galileo first used a small telescope to look into space and since that time man has appreciated that his penetration into space increases with the size of the telescope. The development of the optical telescope, although pioneered in the eighteenth and nineteenth centuries by Lord Rosse and Herschel in the United Kingdom, became the prerogative of the American continent in the twentieth century. The 100-inch telescope on Mount Wilson came into use in 1918, and the 200-inch on Mount Palomar twenty years later.

RADIO WAVES FROM SPACE

For many years it seemed that man's only hope of obtaining information about the stars and the galaxies was by the use of these big optical telescopes. He has evolved with eyes which are sensitive to that part of the spectrum in the visible region between the ultra-violet and infra-red, and it is over this region of the spectrum that a transparency, or window, exists in the earth's atmosphere. If man had evolved with eyes which were sensitive only in the infra-red or ultra-violet then he would have had very little knowledge indeed of outer space until the present day, when it has become possible to move beyond the obscuring region of the atmosphere with satellites and space probes.

Because the earth's atmosphere almost completely obscures any radiation which lies outside the familiar colours of the rainbow it seemed impossible that any useful knowledge of outer space would ever be accumulated in parts of the spectrum other than in this visible gap. This is in spite of the fact that the early researches with radio waves in the 1920s had led to the realization that there was another transparency or gap in the earth's atmosphere at much longer wavelengths in the radio wave region. Whereas the wavelengths of visible light are measured in millionths of a centimetre, the radio wave region, in which there is this other transparency in the atmosphere, extends from a fraction of a centimetre to many metres in wavelength. In the middle of this radio wave band the ordinary broadcasting and television transmissions are made on earth.

Although the existence of this transparency was known, it seemed unlikely that any use could be made of it for astronomical purposes. After all, the stars and the sun are very hot bodies and the fundamental laws of physics indicate that the maximum output of energy from such hot bodies with surface temperatures of many thousands of degrees is in the visible and near visible regions of the spectrum. It was therefore with some incredulity that astronomers received the news in 1931 and 1932 that an electrical engineer, Karl Jansky, who was working at the Bell Telephone Laboratories in America, had detected some radiations or signals in this part of the spectrum which he was convinced had their origin from regions of space outside the solar system. Jansky's apparatus worked on rather a long wavelength between 14 and 20 metres and the aerial consisted of an

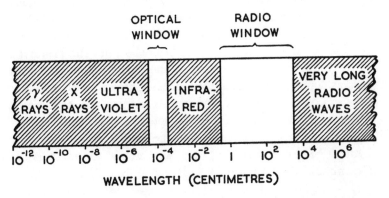

Fig. 2. The complete electromagnetic spectrum showing the regions of transparency of the Earth's atmosphere and ionosphere.

array of rods which could be rotated on a brick foundation. Jansky was investigating the static which was interfering with and limiting the usefulness of radio communications around the world. He discovered that even when there was no obvious form of atmospherics such as a thunderstorm, nevertheless there was a residual disturbance in his receiving apparatus and he noticed that this residual noise in his equipment had a diurnal variation; that is it varied in strength throughout the day. Furthermore he made the classic observation that the maximum in this signal did not come exactly every day at the same time but that it was four minutes earlier each day. This led Jansky to conclude, quite correctly, that the only possibility of explaining this residual noise must be that it was a result of radio waves generated somewhere in regions of space outside the solar system which were being picked up in his aerial system (the reason being that the period of maximum of 23 hours 56 minutes represents the sidereal day, that is the period of rotation of the earth with respect to the stars, and not the solar day of 24 hours). This perfectly simple and straightforward observation of Jansky led to the correct conclusion that the source of this radio noise had its origin not merely in extra-terrestrial space but in extrasolar space, and that it originated either on the stars or in the space between the stars. Astronomers took little notice of Jansky's discovery and the further development of this subject in the years before the second world war was left to an amateur, Grote Reber, who built the prototype of the modern radio telescope in the garden of his home in Illinois. This radio telescope was a bowl, 30 feet in diameter, in the form of a paraboloid, mounted so that it could be directed to any part of the sky. This telescope of Reber's has been re-erected recently as a museum piece at the entrance to the United States National Radio Astronomy Observatory at Greenbank, West Virginia.

THE FIRST RADIO MAP OF THE SKY

With this instrument Reber was able to explore with a reasonable degree of precision the radio waves from the Milky Way, and, indeed, he made the first real map of the radio sky. He confirmed Jansky's conclusion that the noise in his receiver was the result of emissions in the radio wave part of the spectrum picked up from outer space, and he was able to show that the strength of this radio noise depended on the direction in which the beam of his radio telescope was pointing. Reber's radio telescope picked up the radio waves in a beam a few degrees wide. He found that when he directed this beam at the region of the sky where the common visible stars were densest, then his signal strength was greatest. When he directed it to the regions of the Milky Way where the stars were less concentrated, then his signal strength decreased. This seemed a natural result leading to the conclusion that the stars which we see with our eyes in the visible part of the spectrum also emit radio waves. But this picture proved too simple, for when Reber hopefully directed his telescope at some of the bright and nearer stars in the sky such as Sirius and Capella, expecting to be able to find quite strong radio emissions from them, he discovered to his surprise that there were no emissions at all. Thereby he established a paradox which is still not completely resolved, namely that the Milky Way system with its hundred thousand million stars appears to emit radio waves, as well as the light waves by which we see the stars. Although the radio waves are most intense in the regions where there are the most stars, the individual star members do not seem to be radio emitters.

Apart from one or two doubtful and unusual cases this remains the situation today—that nobody has succeeded in detecting radio waves from the individual or common stars which we see by eye in the Milky Way. The sun is an exception; although, for reasons presumably associated with the long period cycle of sunspots, Reber was unable to find any radio emissions from the sun, which itself appears to be an extremely powerful source of radio emission. Indeed, under some conditions, the solar radio waves are so intense that they hinder the investigation of the remote parts of the cosmos. This situation is analogous to the optical case where sunlight makes it impossible to see the faint light of the stars by day. Even if all the stars in the Milky Way system were to emit with the same intensity as the sun, they are so distant and the dilution factor is so great, that there would be no significant contribution to the strength of the signal from the regions of space outside the solar system picked up in a radio telescope. The solution of this paradox seemed to Reber to lie in the following argument. The stars were obviously not emitting radio waves which made a significant contribution to his records but, since there was this close relationship between intensity of the visible light and the strength of the radio emission, the source of the radio waves must be the interstellar hydrogen gas. Since Reber reached that conclusion in the period 1934 to 1938 there have been many changes of opinion about the origin of these radio waves, and now it does seem that Reber was partially correct. First there was a violent swing against this view and it was believed that the interstellar gas did not contribute at all. Now the situation, although extremely complex, involves an explanation in which the radio waves generated in the interstellar hydrogen gas represent a significant component of the extraterrestrial radio emission. The true picture, which is far more exciting than that simple story indicates, will be described in Chapter III.

THE DEVELOPMENT OF THE RADIO TELESCOPE

There was a long hiatus in the development of these discoveries by Jansky and Reber because of the war, but it was the excellence of the techniques and our new ideas about radio and radar which evolved under the stress of military requirements which led to a vigorous resurgence of these studies immediately after the war. It soon became obvious in the early stages of this development that the problem of the radio astronomer was analogous to that of the optical astronomer, namely that large radio telescopes were needed for the same kind of reason that the optical astronomer required large optical instruments. The optical instrument needs a large mirror in order to collect as much light as possible to penetrate further into space, and also to obtain good definition. A similar situation exists with the radio telescope, where it is necessary to collect the radio waves over a big area in order to improve the signal strength of the faint emissions which are generated at great distances in the cosmos, and also because the definition or the resolution of the beam of such a telescope depends directly, for a given wavelength, on the size of the telescope.

Reber's radio telescope was a parabolic bowl 30 feet in diameter. The largest contemporary version of this form of radio telescope is the instrument at Jodrell Bank in which a parabolic bowl 250 feet in diameter is mounted so that it can be directed with precision to any part of the sky. Incoming radiation is reflected from the steel bowl on to the primary feed which is mounted on a mast at the focus 62½ feet from the apex of the paraboloid. Then the signals are transformed by electronic apparatus and recorded. It is possible to direct this bowl to any part of the sky, and for a given wavelength the telescope has something like 8 times the definition and 64 times greater gain than the instrument originally used by Reber. The paraboloidal steel bowl of the radio telescope is formed of 80 tons of steel sheet. This is mounted on a cradle which itself weighs 800 tons and the whole cradle is suspended on trunnion bearings 180 feet above the ground. The elevation drive, or tilt of the bowl, is obtained by electric motors driving through large gun racks, originally part of the *Royal Sovereign* battleship. The 180-ft. towers which support the elevation bearings and motors are connected at ground level by a diametral girder, pivoted at its centre point. The two towers are each carried on six bogies which move on a double railway track 320 feet in diameter so that the instrument can be given rotation or movement in azimuth. The whole superstructure, which moves on the railway track, weighs over 2,000 tons.

On the reverse side of the steel bowl a small hanging laboratory is suspended so that it always remains in the upright position whatever the tilt of the bowl. This is approached by catwalks when the bowl is in the zenith and contains receiving equipment and, if necessary, the observer. Sometimes in order to avoid losses in cables it is necessary to mount the receiving equipment close to the primary feed at the focus. On the top of the aerial tower which rises 62½ ft. from the apex a box about 6-ft. cube is fixed and access to this is obtained by a hydraulic platform from the base of the bowl. This box contains some of the receiving equipment and for some work at high frequencies the aerial itself in the form of a horn feed, as distinct from the common rod dipole, emerges directly from this box.

The control room of the telescope is 200 yards from the superstructure and from a main control desk the controller can command the instrument to perform any motion which the experiment requires. It can be driven separately in azimuth and elevation or a sidereal motion can be obtained by driving through a computer in right ascension and declination. Under those conditions the computer works out the position to which the telescope has to be directed and it will then automatically follow a given star from rising to setting, or a planet, or the sun, depending on the needs of the research programme.

The Jodrell Bank telescope is still the biggest steerable radio telescope, but several specialized instruments have been built which have a better definition and cover a bigger area of ground. These are not generally in this paraboloidal form and they are usually built so that they work in a restricted wavelength range; whereas the great adaptability of the Jodrell Bank instrument and the fact that it can be used as a transmitter as well as a receiver over a very wide range of wavelengths has turned out to be of considerable importance.

Partly because of their association with space probes, radio telescopes have become rather popular instruments. There are now many completely steerable parabolic radio telescopes of size between 50 ft. and 100 ft. in operation, but still very few of larger diameter. The nearest competitor to the Jodrell Bank telescope is the 210-ft. diameter instrument opened in the autumn of 1961 as part of the equipment of the radio astronomy division of the Council for Scientific and Industrial Research Organization in Australia. The Americans are in process of building one of 600 ft. in diameter, at Sugar Grove in West Virginia, but this is primarily a military project; the Russians appear to be operating a steerable telescope with an effective aperture of 140 ft. in their deep-space tracking network.

The optical telescope produces its records on a photographic plate, either of the stars or nebulae themselves, or in the form of spectrographs. The records of the output of the radio telescope generally appear as an ink trace on a paper chart recording the strength of the signal in relation to the time and position of the beam of the telescope. Even for the investigation of a single object such as the M31 nebula in Andromeda it may be necessary to obtain hundreds of these records with the telescope scanning over different parts of the nebula. So one obtains a mosaic from which can be built up a system of isophotes which give the radio picture of the nebula. Nowadays these final processes of treatment of the individual scans are increasingly the subject for computers and other machines which save hundreds of hours of time in the reduction of the basic records.

Experiments of this type with a radio telescope on the Andromeda nebula reveals a very interesting situation which seems to epitomize many of the investigations with radio telescopes, in that they reveal the same kind of paradox as that found in the early work of Reber. Here the radio contours on the whole show a good concentration in the region of the stars which make up the Andromeda nebula, but they also show a considerable intensity of emission at distances which are far removed from anything which the photographic plate records. In fact there appears to be nothing but empty space in regions surrounding the nebula of stars where there is still an intense radio output. We know that both in the M31 nebula and in many of the other extragalactic nebulae which are within the range of our radio observations, the visible stars are surrounded by a corona, or halo, of radio emission which stretches for great distances outside the regions where any matter can be seen in the ordinary photographs. The probable explanation of this emission was suggested by Shklovsky the Russian scientist many years ago. He suggested that these galaxies are surrounded by magnetic fields and that the radio emission is generated by electrons moving at very high speeds in this magnetic field. The interpretation of the contemporary radio picture of the whole sky will be discussed in Chapter III.

THE SPACE PROBE

It is strange that the radio telescopes which were developed to study the radio emissions from space should have become such an essential part of the work of the earth satellite and the space probe. Indeed it is altogether remarkable that, after hundreds of years of the development of the optical telescope as the primary astronomical instrument, man has achieved within the space of a few years two completely new techniques for the exploration of space in the form of the radio telescope and the space probe. The importance of both space probe and earth satellite is that they enable us to take our instruments away from the obscuring layers of the earth's atmosphere into regions outside where we can study the incoming radiation and particles in the planetary system before they are absorbed or distorted by the earth's own atmosphere. The developments in this field since the Russians launched Sputnik I on 4 October 1957 have been tremendous.

The association of the radio telescope with the satellite or space probe arises because the payload can carry only a small amount of weight in spite of the hundreds of tons which have to be lifted from earth by the launching rockets. Thus the transmitter which has to send back to earth the record of the scientific data collected by the instruments in the probe has to be low-powered. The situation is much the same as in the case of the emissions generated naturally in space. There we need a big radio telescope to detect the faint signals and similarly large radio telescopes are required to track the low-powered signals emanating from the probe. The conjunction of the Jodrell Bank telescope with the American space probe Pioneer V enabled the probe to be tracked for four months after it was launched from earth to a distance of nearly 23 million miles. Then some trouble developed in the power supply, the batteries appear to have sprung a leak, and the signals were lost at that stage.

The scientific results with the earth satellites and space probes have revolutionized our ideas about the conditions in the outer regions of the earth's atmosphere and about our immediate environment in space. Perhaps the most remarkable and unexpected of these discoveries was made by the Americans who were behind the Russians in 1957 and whose difficulties were increased by the failure of the early Vanguard launchings in the autumn and winter of 1957. However, in the early hours of the 1st of February, 1958, when the Russians had already launched Sputnik I and Sputnik II, the Americans had their first success with Explorer I. This satellite was launched into an elliptical orbit around the earth with a period of 115 minutes. At its closest approach, the satellite was about 370 kilometres distant whilst its apogee was about 2,500 kilometres away. Amongst the equipment in the satellite Dr. van Allen, of Iowa University, placed a geiger counter which was designed to study the radiations entering the earth's atmosphere from space. At one stage in the early part of this flight records of the telemetry which was being picked up on earth from Explorer I seemed to indicate that this geiger-counter system had failed because it had apparently stopped counting. However, after a time the system recovered and started counting again, sending back to earth records of the number of particles which were incident on the satellite. This process of apparent failure and recovery was repeated and soon it was realized that this was not a fault in the apparatus but that a real effect was occurring. In fact, when the device stopped counting the satellite was passing through a region at a distance of 1,000 kilometres or so from the earth and the cessation of the counting was due to the fact that the radiation on it was so intense that the instrument was blocked. When the satellite was below 1,000 kilometres the system behaved normally and the geiger counter responded in the manner which had been anticipated. It was encased in the steel hull of the satellite and van Allen concluded that the radiation causing the blockage of his equipment must be due to corpuscular radiation of quite unforeseen intensity.

Subsequently this radiation was the subject of intense study by the American earth satellites and deep-space probes and by the Russian Luniks. It seems that as we move out from the earth through the concentration of electrons in the ionized regions which extend to about 400 kilometres, we do not pass into the emptiness of interplanetary space but into regions densely packed with ionized particles. There appear to be two zones surrounding the earth in which ionized particles are trapped by the earth's magnetic field—now commonly known as the van Allen radiation belts or zones. The inner zone is the one first discovered by van Allen, and then the Lunik II and the

Pioneer series of space probes found that at a greater distance from earth there was another distinct zone of trapped charged particles with a different constitution. As a probe moves out from the earth it passes through the electron concentrations at a few hundred kilometres, then on into the first zone of trapped radiation at a few thousand kilometres. The intensity then decreases, but soon rises again to a much greater strength at a

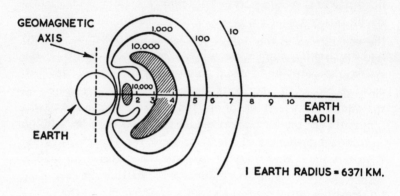

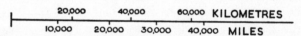

Fig. 3. A cross-section of a three-dimensional figure of revolution around the Earth's geomagnetic axis, showing the intensity of the trapped radiation around the Earth. The numbers on the contours are the counts/second recorded by the radiation counter and indicate the relative intensity of radiation in the zones.
(*After Professor J. A. van Allen*)

distance 20,000 to 30,000 kilometres from the earth. The exact situation is complicated; for example, it is probable that this outer zone has more than one maximum in it, and whereas the inner zone seems to be stable, the outer one is variable both in extent and concentration.

What is responsible for this intense radiation in these zones? The following facts are so far established with some certainty. The particles in the inner zone are protons, nuclei of the hydrogen atom, trapped in the earth's geomagnetic field. There are a few electrons trapped in this zone but not very many; it is almost overwhelmingly constituted of protons. On the other hand, the outer zone is almost entirely constituted of electrons, and there are a very few protons in it. The energies of the particles in these zones compared with the energies which one can generate on earth in the contemporary accelerating machines are low. For example, the energies of the protons in the inner zone do not exceed 100 megavolts and the energies of the electrons in the outer zone are less than 100 kilovolts. On the other hand the number of particles is enormous. In the inner zone the flux of protons is about $2 \times 10^4/cm.^2/sec.$, and the flux of electrons in the outer zone is something like 10^{11} electrons/cm.^{2}/sec. These numbers have to be compared with the flux of cosmic ray particles from space—about two protons and heavy nuclei/cm.^{2}/sec., representing the extent of the radiation to be anticipated in these regions. It is the quantity rather than the energy which gives the radiation zones this special importance and, indeed, danger to living organisms. In terms of common radiation dosage, cosmic rays represent about 0.01 roentgen/hour, compared with the permissible human dosage of 0.3 roentgen/week. In the heart of the outer radiation zone, the dose is about 10 roentgen/hour—5,000 times greater than a human being could stand.

The origin of the particles in these radiation zones is not yet finally resolved. The inner zone of protons is stable and constant. This zone seems to contain the same kind of energetic particles and about the same quantity whenever it has been investigated. It is believed that the protons in this zone arise from the decay of neutrons which are moving out of the atmosphere of the earth, and that the neutrons responsible are some of the products of nuclear disintegrations produced in the earth's atmosphere by cosmic ray bombardment. In contrast to the stability of the inner zone, the outer zone of electrons is extremely unstable and is influenced in some detail by events on the sun. Solar flares and magnetic storms appear to have a controlling influence on this zone of electrons. For example, it has been found that a big magnetic storm on the earth drains the electrons from this zone.

After a few days the zone recovers, presumably repopulated with electrons from the sun. Cause and effect are not yet distinguished, but it is clear that this outer radiation zone is closely linked with the major geophysical effects observed on earth, such as magnetic storms and the aurora polaris. It seems that this outer zone acts in the role of a reservoir of charged particles with the sun as the source and the earth as the sink.

It seems likely that the regions of space containing the outer limits of the radiation zones, 50,000 kilometres from the earth, are the regions where outer space can really be said to begin. This is where the solar wind, consisting of streams of electrons continuously blown out from the solar atmosphere (with particular intensity during solar eruptions), reach a compromise with the earth's own geophysical environment. Only a few years ago we would have talked about outer space beginning just above the ionospheric regions—only 400 or 500 kilometres above the earth's surface. Now we must think in terms of outer space beginning in the region of 60,000 or 70,000 kilometres from the earth. Moreover, we begin to visualize the earth and planets as bodies enveloped in the solar atmosphere, closely under solar control, in the environmental as well as the gravitational sense.

II

THE SOLAR SYSTEM

URING the last few years there has been a renewal of
interest in the problems of the solar system. This new
interest has been stimulated by the discoveries made by
using space probes and by the results of research programmes
of the radio telescopes, which have revealed many new facts
about our immediate environment in space, the explanations
for which are not yet understood.

The basic astronomical data about the solar system are well
known. The earth, moving in a nearly circular orbit 93,000,000
miles from the sun, is a member of the sun's family of planets.
Mercury, at a mean distance of 36,000,000 miles from the
sun, and Venus at a mean distance of 67,200,000 miles, are
in orbits closer to the sun. The orbit of Mars lies outside that
of the earth at a mean distance of 141,500,000 miles. Then
comes the outer planetary system of giants: Jupiter, 483,000,000
miles from the sun, Saturn (886,000,000 miles), Uranus (1,783
million miles), Neptune (2,793 million miles), and Pluto (3,666
million miles).

The inferior planets—Mercury, Venus, Earth, and Mars,
are distinguishable from the giants by the fact that they have
approximately the same size and density—compared with the
earth as unity, the densities range from 0.69 for Mars to
1.1 for Mercury, and the diameters from 0.37 for Mercury to
0.97 for Venus. The giant planets are in a different category,
with densities much smaller than the earth (from 0.13 for
Saturn to 0.25 for Jupiter), but they are of enormous size
ranging from Uranus which is four times the diameter of the
earth, to Jupiter, over eleven times the earth's diameter. The
outermost planet Pluto is exceptional: although its dimensions
are not accurately known, it must be small, with the highest-
known density in the solar system. Between the inferior and

17

giant planets, that is, between the orbits of Mars and Jupiter, there is a swarm of minor planets, or asteroids, the largest of which is Ceres with a diameter of 400 - 500 miles, but many are probably only a few miles in diameter. The number of asteroids is not known but there are probably between 50,000 and 100,000.

The dimensions of the solar system are determined by the extreme orbit of Pluto which is slightly elliptical. Although

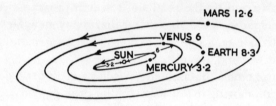

THE FOUR INNER PLANETS

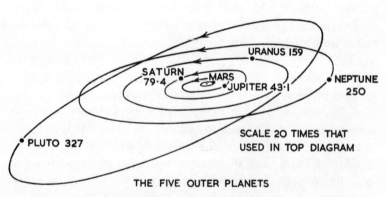

THE FIVE OUTER PLANETS

Fig. 4. The Solar System. Numbers give the distance of the planet from the Sun in light minutes.

at its closest approach to the sun the orbit of Pluto lies inside that of Neptune, the most distant point of its orbit takes it 4,566 million miles away. At this point the light from the sun to Pluto takes about 6½ hours on its journey. And so the size of the earth's abode in space is epitomized by the 93,000,000 miles or 8 light minutes which separate us from the sun and the 6½ light hours of the furthest point of Pluto's orbit from the sun. Although these distances are enormous by terrestrial standards it has to be remembered that once we move out from this system we have to travel for 4½ years at the speed of light before we get to the nearest star and then for 100,000 years to the extreme reaches of the galaxy.

The parent of the solar system—the sun—has a diameter of 865,000 miles (that is excluding the solar atmosphere) and is 332,000 times the mass of the earth. The weight of the sun is about 10^{24} tons; that is, a few thousand, billion, billion tons. The energy output of the sun is about 10^{20} or 100 million billion kilowatt hours per second. This energy is produced by thermonuclear processes which convert 4 million tons of the solar matter into energy every second. The conversion takes place in the centre of the sun where the temperature is about 20 million degrees centigrade and the pressures amount to several thousand million atmospheres. Under these conditions the atoms are stripped of electrons and matter is degenerate. These transmutations in the interior of the sun involve the conversion of 564 million tons of hydrogen to 560 million tons of helium every second. Although the solar material is being used at this rate the processes have already been operative for at least 4,000 million years. The sun's mass is so tremendous that this rate of use of its material represents only about one-tenth per cent. of its mass every ten thousand million years.

THE INTERPLANETARY SPACE

Until quite recently we have tended to think of the space between the sun and the earth and the planets as being empty— a near vacuum, not possessing many factors of interest to geophysics or astronomy. We were aware that the earth was surrounded by the ionosphere—a region of electrons of varying density extending to a few hundred kilometres above the earth's surface—and that the density of electrons in these regions appeared to be related to the condition of the solar surface and

to be generally under solar control. Apart from this, the various
bodies seemed to be rather disconnected except for the
gravitational forces which controlled their motions. One of the
most remarkable changes of opinion during the last few years
is in respect of this situation in interplanetary space, because it
now appears that this space is not empty. On the contrary, the
interplanetary space must now be visualized as a medium,
where the conflict of a complex of radiation, ionized particles,
and magnetic forces is determining the geophysical environment of the earth and the planets.

THE SOLAR ATMOSPHERE

The discovery of the ionized particles trapped in the van
Allen belts around the earth has led to a searching inquiry
regarding their origin. As already mentioned (Chapter I), the
inner belt seems to be composed chiefly of protons which are
believed to be the decay products of neutrons moving out from
the atmosphere of the earth, where they have been produced
by cosmic ray bombardment. The outer zone of electrons is
unstable and the present theory of the origin of the electrons
is that they are part of the stream of material which is being
blown away from the sun. It is possible that in the region of
about 10 earth radii we have the interfacial boundary, where
the earth's own environment is coming to terms with these
solar forces. The sun has an intensely hot central region where
the thermonuclear energy-producing processes are taking place.
However, its surface temperature as observed from earth
through ordinary optical instruments is about 6,000°. Systematic
observation of this solar surface reveals a number of variable
features. The most striking is the apparition of sunspots, whose
appearance on the disc varies in an eleven-year cycle. Although
sunspots were observed by Galileo—who was involved in a
bitter dispute with Father Scheiner over the priority of discovery
—their origin and nature are still not fully understood.
Occasionally, when there is a big group of sunspots, a solar flare
occurs, accompanied by a violent ejection of hydrogenous
material. The study of sunspots and solar flares with spectro-

helioscopes and other optical instruments has in recent years been supplemented by radio astronomical studies. One of the earliest discoveries made during the rapid development of radio astronomy after the war was that sunspots, and particularly on the occasions when they associated to such an extent that a big flare occurred, generated powerful radio waves. Many types of intense and sporadic radio wave emissions from the sun are now recognized, in association with disturbances on the solar surface. The corona or atmosphere of the sun also generates radio waves which, although much weaker than the irregular outbursts, are present all the time. When the sun is eclipsed the vast gaseous layer of the corona can be seen streaming out to a few solar radii. This coronal gas is in a state of turbulent motion and the conditions are such that at about half a solar radius above the visible disc there are about 30 million atoms per c.c. and the effective temperature is a few million degrees absolute. These conditions create a most interesting situation and recent calculations indicate that there is a resultant outward pressure which causes the material of the solar corona to expand outwards continually with a speed of between 500 to 1,500 km./sec. This streaming material is known as the solar wind. The experimental evidence for the existence of this solar wind has, until recently, been rather scarce, but in the spring of 1961 the Americans launched a space probe equipped with instruments specifically designed to detect the existence and measure the constitution of this material streaming from the sun. Although the probe stayed up for only about 48 hours it succeeded in its task of recording and measuring the existence of the solar wind in the interplanetary space. The situation which occurs when sunspots and flares are seen on the solar disc is a violent modulation of this steady streaming away from the sun, because on these occasions the material of the corona and chromosphere is ejected at velocities several times that of the normal streaming velocity of the coronal material.

Another intriguing new concept concerns the behaviour of magnetic fields. Hitherto we have tended to visualize magnetic fields as entities belonging to a magnet whose magnetic field moved with it. Astronomically it was believed that magnetic fields were localized in bodies like the earth, the sun and some of the stars. Now it is realized that if there is a gas in a highly ionized condition, like the material of the solar wind, moving in interplanetary space where the free path is thousands of kilometres, then this material which is streaming away carries its own magnetic field. This concept of the trapped magnetic field—contained in a stream of gas, coming from the solar corona or from the shell of a star, moving away into space so that the ionized particles and the magnetic field move together, actually being transported through space to another part of the solar system or another part of the cosmos—has become of great importance in theoretical astrophysics. The possibility of magnetic fields moving in this way with the gas appears to be one of the controlling influences which may govern the organization of the solar system and indeed of the cosmos as a whole. In particular the fact that this gas streaming from the sun carries with it a magnetic field is a matter of great importance as far as the earth is concerned, because when this solar wind reaches the neighbourhood of the earth then the earth's magnetic field is disturbed. The electrons which are streaming away from the sun can then be injected into the earth's own magnetic field; they become trapped in it and in this way the outer layer of the van Allen belts is probably formed. These ideas provide a good explanation of the situation whereby this outer belt of electrons is so subject to solar control, why it disappears in a magnetic storm, and the processes by which it is repopulated after a matter of some days. In principle the earth's field should present a fairly solid barrier against the injection of particles of comparatively low energy from outside, but it is this distortion of the magnetic field by the travelling fields coming away from the sun which facilitates the injection.

The whole phenomenon of the earth's magnetic storms and the aurora borealis, or the northern lights, must be tied up with these particles which are trapped in the van Allen belts. The aurorae were known to be associated with solar flares and it was believed that the phenomena were caused by the particles streaming out from the region of the flare on the sun and reaching the neighbourhood of the earth after a period of 24 to 30 hours, when they entered the atmosphere and gave rise to ionization at a height of 100 kilometres or so. This explanation is now obviously incorrect because it is known that the particles from the sun are trapped in the outer van Allen belt. The formation of the aurora seems to be associated with the draining of the particles from the outer belt during a magnetic storm. Apparently the primary aurora particles do originate in this outer belt and the function of the magnetic storm in the aurora phenomenon is to produce the magnetically disturbed condition which allows the particles to escape from the belt and enter the atmosphere down the earth's own lines of force.

The phenomenon of the travelling solar magnetic field is of great interest in many other aspects of physics, particularly in cosmic ray physics. The primary cosmic ray particles are believed to be generated in the galaxy and it has been known for a long time that their intensity, incident on the earth's atmosphere, decreased when there was a severe magnetic disturbance. This effect was so closely linked with the modulation of the earth's field that it had been assumed to be a local terrestrial effect, in that the variation of the cosmic ray intensity was governed by the changes in the earth's field. During 1960 and 1961 Simpson of Chicago discovered, by cosmic ray-counting experiments in the American space probes Explorer VI and Pioneer V, that this decrease observed on earth was accompanied by a simultaneous decrease in the counting rate of the apparatus in the probes when they were many millions of kilometres away in interplanetary space. Clearly, it is the variation in the magnetic field in interplanetary space itself which is controlling this intensity variation and not the local field of the earth, and the variable interplanetary fields of this nature must arise through the magnetic field trapped in the material streaming away from the sun.

In addition to the material which streams away from the solar corona, and the high energy protons which are ejected at the time of solar flares, the sun frequently ejects large quantities of low energy protons. All these radiations present a serious hazard to the astronaut intending to travel in interplanetary space and considerable thought is already being given to possibilities of predicting the nature and timing of these solar outbursts.

Whereas the space probes have become avenues through which we are learning about the influence of the sun in interplanetary space, the observations of the solar radio emissions have revolutionized our picture of the sun itself. The powerful emissions of radio waves during sunspots and solar flares are the most obvious radio phenomena associated with the sun. But the observation of the less intense radio emissions from the solar corona has revealed an interesting situation. If we imagine ourselves looking at the sun with radio eyes instead of with ordinary eyes, then we would observe quite a different object in the sky. At a wavelength of 21 cm., instead of the uniform disc which we usually see, its appearance would be that of a disc that was brighter towards the edges and was flattened instead of circular. It would extend much further into space than it does when visually observed. If our eyes were tuned to look at a rather longer wavelength in the metre waveband then we should begin to think that the sun was monopolizing the whole sky. On wavelengths of several metres the corona of the sun, or the radio sun, has been traced out to something like 20 or 30 solar radii. All this is compatible with the picture we have already formed of the influence of the solar atmosphere extending throughout great distances of interplanetary space.

METEORS OR SHOOTING STARS

In addition to the complex of radiation and ionized particles in space, there is a vast debris of small particles mainly composed of stone or iron. The most common manifestation of these is the appearance in the sky of a meteor or shooting star. Occasionally the particles are so big that they penetrate the atmosphere and fall to the earth as meteorites. The common shooting stars occur when the earth encounters this debris in its journey through space ; the particles are heated by friction as they enter the outer layers of the atmosphere, and have generally evaporated completely at about 100 kilometres above the surface of the earth, leaving behind a transient trail of light. The occurrence of these meteors has been known for centuries and they may be seen in any clear dark sky with the naked eye at a rate of about 10 per hour. These are the sporadic meteors which appear to be distributed with a fair degree of uniformity in interplanetary space. On the other hand at particular times of the year, say in August or in December, the rate rises to 50 to 100 per hour for a few nights. These are the shower meteors which appear to radiate from a particular point in the sky and generally occur with considerable regularity from year to year.

The question of the origin of these meteors in the solar system is another problem of great contemporary interest. The earth moves in its orbit around the sun at a speed of about 29 km./ sec.; as well as this motion of the earth round the sun, the sun itself and the entire solar system is moving through space with a velocity of about 20 km./sec., in the direction of the star Vega. To an observer outside the solar system the motion of the earth would appear to be like that of a giant corkscrew. In this journey the earth occasionally runs into the streams of debris which are concentrated in orbits around the sun. These enter the atmosphere of the earth and give rise to the showers of meteors.

These concentrations of debris are, in many cases, closely associated with comets. Although the origin of the comets is uncertain, we know that they are contained within the solar system moving under the gravitational control of the sun and are not visitors from interstellar space. The nucleus of the comet is an icy conglomerate of various organic compounds, and most of the comets have a long tail which may stream behind the head for millions of kilometres. In this tail or in the orbit of the comet we have these very large numbers of small specks of dust which may have been evaporated from the nucleus as the comet approaches the sun. One comet which has been of considerable contemporary interest in the study of meteors during the last decade is the Giacobini-Zinner Comet. In October 1946 the earth crossed the orbit of the comet only a few days from the position of the nucleus. For a few hours between midnight and 6 a.m. on 10 October thousands of meteors could be seen in the sky, but before this and afterwards the meteor rate was of the usual sporadic value of a few per hour. This was a clear and spectacular demonstration of the close relationship between meteors and comets.

The systematic study of meteors has been severely handicapped by the difficulty of making observations, as the sky is so frequently either obscured by cloud or made light by moonlight. Radio astronomy has given us new methods of investigating these meteors which overcome the difficulty of cloud, moonlight, or daylight. When the meteoric particle evaporates in the high atmosphere it leaves behind a trail of ionized particles as well as the luminous trail by which we see it. The electrons in this ionized trail are efficient scatterers of radio waves. A beam of radio waves transmitted from a radio telescope is scattered by the trail and the returned signal can be detected by the receiving part of the telescope equipment as a transient echo. If the recording equipment consists of a cathode ray tube with a suitable time base, it is possible to observe the diffraction pattern which is formed as the ionized trail crosses the perpendicular from the receiver to the trail. This is the radio analogue of the diffraction of light at a straight edge—the rhythmic variations in brightness as the shadow merges into the light. In the radio case, since the range can be measured and the wavelength is known, the precise velocity of the meteor can be determined. If these observations are made from three spaced receiving stations using one transmitter, the exact orbit in space of a single meteoric particle can be obtained.

The relative infrequency of the meteors seen by a single observer gives a false impression of the vast numbers which the earth encounters in its journey through space. The number entering the earth's atmosphere which are big enough to produce a trail sufficiently bright to be seen in a small telescope is about 8,000 million every day. These are small grains of dust weighing only about a ten-thousandth of a gram. Using radio techniques one can detect particles of even smaller size, and the numbers increase by about 2½ times for every fainter magnitude. The particles detected by the most sensitive radio-meteor equipment available today are probably being swept up by the earth at the rate of about a million million per day. The numbers seem to increase endlessly as the size goes down, but when the radius of the particles is less than about a millimetre then these particles are too small to burn up. For these the ratio of the surface area to the mass is so large that the energy of interaction when the particles begin to enter the atmosphere is radiated away and the flight of the dust grain is stopped before evaporation occurs. These are the micrometeorites which eventually fall to earth as dust. From a study of the deposits on the ocean bed it has been estimated that the earth collects something like a million tons per annum in this way.

The micrometeorites are now the subject of investigations using satelites and space probes, and many space vehicles launched by the Americans and Russians have been equipped with some form of micrometeorite detector. In principle, the detection of these micrometeorites in space should be simple— by allowing them to collide with a diaphragm which is equipped with a microphone: when a dust grain hits the diaphragm it will make a sound in the microphone and be telemetred back to earth. In practice these impact methods have proved to be difficult because the microphones record noises other than the impact of the dust grains; the calibration, too, is uncertain. The techniques have now been refined and we have some idea of the amount of dust of this extraordinarily small size which exists in space. For particles which weigh a hundred millionth of a gram the rate of impact is found to be equivalent to one particle per 1,000 sec. over a surface of area 1 square inch. For particles which weigh a thousand millionth of a gram the rate is found to be 1 every 100 sec. The quantity of this dust is 1,000 to 10,000 times greater than the particles which are big enough to burn up in the atmosphere.

From some of the recent analyses of the micrometeorite recordings in the American satelites, Whipple of Harvard has concluded that a very large quantity of this small dust appears to be travelling in an orbit around the earth. It appears that in some circumstances which are not yet understood some of this fine dust gets trapped in gravitational orbits around the earth. So we seem to have two new situations arising. We have the trapped radiation, the protons and electrons in the van Allen belts (that is a magnetic trapping), and also a gravitational trapping of very fine dust in the vicinity of the earth.

At the other end of the scale of size, as the particles become bigger their numbers decrease. Objects which we see in the sky as bright fireballs probably weigh about a gram, and there may be a million of these entering the earth's atmosphere every day. If the meteor is much larger than this it will not be completely evaporated in its journey through the atmosphere and some part of it will fall to earth as a solid body. Something like 500 kilograms of this material per year fall to earth in this way as meteorites. Occasionally these meteorites are extremely big and there are classic examples such as the meteor crater in Arizona and the Siberian meteorite which fell in 1919 and devastated 100 square miles of countryside. If ever a meteorite of this size fell on a populated area then there would indeed be a calamity, but oddly enough there seems to be no well attested case of anyone being killed by a meteorite fall. Some years ago a person in America was injured by a meteorite but even this was from the first bounce of a small fragment. There has been some discussion about the dangers of these meteors and meteorites to space travellers, but the chances of being hit by anything which could do serious damage to a space ship is so small that none of the experts really worry about it. Of course the astronauts who land on the moon will need protection, because there is no atmosphere to act as a shield even from the micro-meteorites.

The refinement of the measurements made in space probes and satellites, coupled with further development in the ground-based photographic and radio-echo meteor work, will certainly lead to a much better understanding of the role of these particles in the formation and evolution of the solar system. At present it is believed that the large meteorites which fall to earth have a different origin from the meteors. Are the meteorites an extension of the size range of meteors, or are they a separate class? Does all this debris represent samples of the primeval material left over from the formation of the solar system or is it the consequence of some subsequent planetary catastrophe? It is clear that an extraordinarily complex situation exists in the solar system in the space between the earth and planets and the sun, not only of electromagnetic radiation but of corpuscular radiation, and of solid material particles in the form of dust and pieces of stone and iron.

THE MOON AND THE PLANETS

The techniques of radio astronomy and the space probe seem to be on the verge of increasing markedly our knowledge of the moon and the planets. For example, in the case of the moon, the radio astronomical work has already given some extremely interesting results. Ten years ago it was a difficult technological problem to transmit radio waves from earth and pick them up again $2\frac{1}{2}$ seconds later after they had been reflected from the surface of the moon nearly a quarter of a million miles distant. Now, with the large radio telescopes, this is an easy technical task but, as so often happens with new scientific experiments, completely unexpected effects were encountered. The moon appears to be fairly uniformly bright to the eye, and it was assumed that if radio waves of uniform strength were transmitted to the moon, then they would be scattered uniformly from the lunar surface so that the signals collected by the radio telescope and recorded as echoes on a cathode ray tube would always be of the same strength. It was surprising to find that this was not the situation. The transmissions from the telescope were made in the form of short pulses which were expected to be recorded as pulses of uniform strength after scattering from the lunar surface. In fact, very marked irregularities in the strength of the returned echoes were found. The individual pulses, separated in time by a second or so, varied in strength and there was also a long-period variation in the average strength of the returned signals with periods of 15 or 30 minutes. It appears that these short-period and long-period effects are quite different phenomena. The long-period variation is the result of an influence on the radio waves of the earth's magnetic field as they traverse the space between the earth and the moon. Most of this influence occurs in the ionized regions of the earth at a height of about 200 to 400 kilometres, and the variation is caused by the rotation of the plane of polarization of the radio waves—the Faraday effect occurring in the earth's ionosphere. The exploitation of this effect in a systematic manner has provided a method of measuring the total number of electrons between the earth and the moon.

The short-period fading which takes place in periods of seconds has a different origin. This fading is an effect of the libration of the moon. Because of the irregularities of the slight ellipticity of the motion of the moon around the earth, it never presents exactly the same face but gives the effect of a slight oscillation known as libration. It seems that the nature of the lunar surface is such that even for radio wavelengths it does not reflect as a smooth body but has a number of plateaux which reflect the radio waves back to earth. The reflecting qualities of adjacent parts of the lunar surface differ so much that we get these very large variations in amplitude. An investigation of the statistics of this phenomenon leads to a surprising conclusion. In the case of the reflection of light, the moon behaves like a ball of chalk which would appear uniformly bright in a beam of light. On the other hand, when radio waves are directed towards it the moon scatters similarly to a polished ballbearing in a beam of light—the central region of the ball appearing much brighter than the remainder of the surface. When radio waves are reflected from the moon it seems that they are not scattered uniformly from the whole forward hemisphere of the moon but are scattered predominantly from a small part of the forward hemisphere—a hemispherical cap only about a fifth of the radius of the lunar surface. This is a striking illustration of the unexpected roughness of the moon as far as wavelengths of the order of a metre or so are concerned.

This discovery had had an interesting practical result. The suitability of the moon had often been considered in relation to the problem of bouncing radio messages from one side of the earth to the other, using radio wavelengths so short that the earth's ionosphere was penetrated and therefore there could be no interference from sunspots. It had been decided that this was impossible because the moon, reflecting over such a large area, would introduce so much distortion that the signals would be unintelligible. However, the conclusion reached from the study of the short-period fluctuations that only the central part of the lunar hemisphere was effective, entirely altered this situation, and it seemed at least possible that if one modulated the radio waves going out from the radio telescope with speech instead of with the pulses, then one might at least be able to get back intelligible speech reflected from the moon. This proved to be the case, and it is now possible to converse intelligibly between any two points of the world, from which it is mutually visible, by using the moon as a reflecting surface.

Radio telescopes have been used to measure the radio emissions from several of the planets in the region of centimetre wavelengths. This is the thermal emission appropriate to the temperature of the body, and useful comparisons with the temperatures derived by optical studies are being made. More surprising is the detection of large sporadic outbursts on long wavelengths from Jupiter. The energies involved in the generation of these radio waves must be enormous. There is some evidence that the events occur on the surface of the planet rather than in its atmosphere. Should this be the case, the forces at work must be equivalent to the energies involved in several hydrogen bombs, or in giant volcanic eruptions like the explosion of Krakatoa.

The extension of the lunar radar experiments to the nearer planets presented a major challenge. The moon is 240,000 miles distant and the return journey of the radio waves from earth takes 2½ seconds. At close approach Venus is nearly 30,000,000 miles away and the radar signal would take over 5 minutes on the journey there and back to earth. In terms of sensitivity of apparatus it is ten million times more difficult to achieve success here than with the lunar echo. However, a beginning has been made. An American team with a transmitter of very great power on an 80-ft. radio telescope, and a team at Jodrell Bank using a smaller transmitter on the 250-ft. radio telescope, have both achieved initial success in these Venus experiments. Even with these preliminary results a direct measurement of the distance of the planet has been made and the range of uncertainty about the value of the solar parallax has been significantly reduced. It is hoped that in the near future further extension of this work will enable the rate of rotation of the planet to be measured. It is likely, too, that the experiments will give some guidance on the nature of the surface of the planet.

At the moment no one can be sure whether the first determination of the rotation period of Venus will come from these radio-astronomical studies or from instruments carried in a space probe, which either orbits or makes a close approach to the planet. There are, however, many aspects of these lunar and planetary studies which can only be achieved by the physical presence of instruments carried in space probes. Lunik II crashed its instruments on to the lunar surface. Soon we may expect control to be exercised in the final stages of flight. Then either a soft landing can be made and the instruments maintained in working order on the lunar surface, or the probe can be placed in close orbit around the moon. Then we shall have the potential for studying the lunar atmosphere and magnetic field (if any exists); and of making detailed measurements on the lunar surface, which may well have a decisive influence on many outstanding conflicts of opinion. The history of many aeons of time is contained on the lunar surface, which must be almost untouched by erosion. Is there, for example, an identity of material between the meteorites which crash to earth and the surface of the moon? The analysis of certain meteorites made by Urey seems to indicate that at some stage in their history they must have gone through processes of heating which could only occur in the interior of a body of lunar size; and that these meteorites which we handle today are the result of a shattering of these moons in collision. If this is correct there must, at some stage in the evolution of the solar system, have been at least ten objects the size of the present moon which eventually disintegrated in mutual collisions. It seems that these lunar investigations may well hold the key to a major problem in the evolution of the solar system.

THE ORIGIN OF THE SOLAR SYSTEM

Various forms of evidence indicate that the earth is about 4,500 million years old. In the first half of this century we believed that the earth and the planets were torn out of the sun in the form of great tongues of solar gas by the gravitational attraction of a passing star. The wandering star passed on its journey and eventually after aeons of time the molten gas cooled down and formed the planets and the earth. One significant feature of this theory was that the close encounter of two stars in this way must be an extremely rare accident and in spite of the trillions of stars in the universe the solar system was probably unique. Today we are aware of reasons why the earth and the planets could not have been torn from the sun in this way. For example, 98 per cent. of the mass of the entire solar system is in the sun, but 98 per cent. of the angular momentum of the system resides in the planets. Since the division of angular momenta must have occurred at the time of formation of the solar system, this represents an impossible situation. Gaseous material torn out from the sun with that distribution of momenta could not possibly have aggregated into planets.

Today we believe that the solar system was formed in quite a different way. Originally, the sun, which is an average star, was probably surrounded by a nebula of dust and gas. These particles of dust suffered collisions with one another and a certain degree of accretion or coagulation occurred. This process continued through a thousand million years or so, the coagulations all the time getting bigger and bigger, with fragmentation occurring as the larger particles collided. Eventually these became powerful accretors of material, and it is possible dynamically to explain with some degree of precision how the planets of various sizes and mass were formed in this manner.

One uncertainty in the argument concerns the process by which the sun collected the original nebula of gas and dust. There seem to be two possibilities. Interstellar space is full of clouds of dust, and it may be that the sun as it journeyed through space ran into one of these very dense clouds and carried with it this large nebula which must at that time have spread over billions of miles representing the extent of planetary orbits. Or it is possible that the event which gives rise to the birth of a star like the sun involves the simultaneous creation of thousands of stars from the primeval cloud of hydrogenous material, and that so much dust and gaseous material remains that the stars themselves are left with a nebula of gas and dust as part of this formation process.

There are important consequences of these new ideas. On the former ideas that the planets were torn out of the sun, the orgin of the solar system was a rare accident; it must have been unique in the entire universe in spite of the vast numbers of stars which existed. In this theory the earth must originally have been extremely hot, and therefore all the biological processes which have since occurred must have been events which took place subsequent to the cooling down of the earth. On the accretion theory the situation is quite different. The formation of planetary systems from the nebulae around stars may be a frequent occurrence in the universe, and our own solar system can no longer be regarded as unique. Another important corollary is that this accretion of planetary systems occurs in a cold state and any prebiotic material which exists on the interstellar dust of the nebulae will be carried over to the planets. The significance of these new ideas is developed in Chapter V.

III
THE STRUCTURE OF
THE UNIVERSE

THE discovery of radio waves originating in space and the
advent of the larger radio telescopes has had a major
impact on the investigation of the regions of the universe
which lie beyond the solar system. The space probes have not
yet penetrated very far into the solar system, and so far have not
produced any really striking new information about the regions
of space outside the solar system. It must be remembered, however, that the possibility of orbiting telescopes outside the earth's
atmosphere, and of establishing an optical telescope on the
moon, might revolutionize optical astronomy by removing one
of its severest handicaps—the bad visibility caused by the
earth's atmosphere. Here, we are mainly concerned with the new
discoveries of the radio telescope and with the interpretation of
these discoveries in relation to the universe which is revealed in
the large optical telescopes.

THE ARRANGEMENT OF THE STARS IN THE GALAXIES

Photographs of the Milky Way show the apparent existence of
great rifts which appear in the distribution of its 100,000 million
stars. At one time it was believed that these rifts were real in the
sense that there was an avoidance of stars in those directions, but
this certainly is not the case. It is now clear that these dark
patches which you can see by eye as the great divide of the Milky
Way in the direction of Sagittarius are caused by enormous
clouds of dust which exist in the space between the stars. From
the optical point of view this dust is a most tremendous
handicap. By terrestrial standards there is very little of it;
one tiny speck of microscopic dust every few cubic centimetres
of space. Even so, the volumes of space are so great that this
dust obscures about 99 per cent. of starlight. If all this dust

were removed we would find that the starlight became brighter than the full moon. Unfortunately, from the optical point of view, these great clouds of dust lie in the plane of the galactic system, and the sun is far out on one of the spiral arms of the disc so that our view of the central regions of the galaxy is seriously obscured.

Neither the dust in our own atmosphere nor the dust in inter-stellar space hinders the passage of radio waves and one of the great triumphs of radio astronomy is its ability to penetrate the interstellar dust, revealing the structure of the parts of the Milky Way which are obscured from our eyes. Until the advent of radio telescopes the ironical situation existed that although the optical telescopes showed quite clearly the spiral formation of the arrangement of stars in the external galaxies, millions of light years distant, there was uncertainty as to whether the stars in our own Milky Way system were arranged in the same spiral formation. There was certain optical evidence to strengthen the belief that the stars in the Milky Way system were rather similarly arranged to those in the Andromeda nebula, but there was no conclusive information about this. So much seemed to be similar between the Milky Way system of stars and many of these spiral nebulae which can be seen clearly in the telescopes at distances of a few million light years, that it was a natural and reasonable assumption that our system was arranged in this way.

In these nebulae, like M31 in Andromeda, a dense central nucleus of stars has the spiral arms emerging from it, and in such a system the solar system would be far out in one of the arms 30,000 light years distant from the nucleus of the galaxy. In the case of the local Milky Way system, the whole galaxy is rotating like a giant cartwheel and the solar system is moving with it, rotating once in 250 million years. Since the birth of the sun we have rotated 25 times in this enormous journey in space. The motion of ourselves on earth through space is a matter of extreme complexity. We are orbiting around the sun at 29 km./sec. in our annual journey; the sun itself has a proper motion within the system of stars in the Milky Way system at a speed of 20 km./sec. towards Vega; and on top of that the whole solar system is engaged in this extraordinary cosmical rotation, which occurs once every 250 million years. Now we know that the arms in our own system are trailing, and moreover it is as though the galaxy were fluid, and not rigid, so that the speed at the edge of the arms is about twice as great as the speed of rotation of the material near the nucleus of the galaxy.

The Milky Way contains stars which cover a wide variety of types from those which have about a hundredth of the luminosity of the sun to some which are a hundred times its size. The brightness and mass of these stars covers an enormous range. There are some stars in our own system which are so big that on the scale of the solar system they would envelop the orbits of the outer planets—certainly as far out as Saturn. On the other hand, others are only a hundredth of the size of the sun but nevertheless have the same amount of material in them. These objects, the white dwarfs, are incredibly dense. There, matter is degenerate and the density of their cores must be tens of thousands of times greater than the density of water. A common example is that in the star which is the companion of Sirius, a ton of the material would only occupy the space of a matchbox.

Not all the nebulae have their stars arranged in spiral form. Some, although showing slight signs of a spiral formation, are rather irregular. Many other nebulae show no signs of spiral formation but are spheroidal or ellipsoidal with no arms and no obvious structure. The Andromeda nebula, M31, has two small companions which are elliptical galaxies. The arrangement of these galaxies in space and the question of their evolution is reserved for Chapter IV.

THE RADIO EMISSIONS FROM SPACE

Many new problems have been presented to us by the observations of the radio telescopes. The basic paradox has been described in Chapter I. The strength of the radio waves picked up by the radio telescope receiving in a narrow beam varies markedly as it points to different parts of the heavens. On the whole, the signals seem to vary in accordance with the concentration of the visible stars—but the individual stars do not contribute to the emission. As the beam of the telescope moves across the galactic plane, for example, the signal strength increases slowly and within a degree or so of the plane there is a sharp increase in signal strength.

A series of scans at different galactic longitudes readily illustrates the fact that the strongest radio signals come from the direction of the galactic nucleus. This situation is nearly the same as that shown by the contours of the starlight—particularly if an allowance is made for the effect of obscuration by the dust. The most obvious explanation—that the stars are emitting radio signals as well as the light by which we see them—can readily be dismissed by pointing the radio telescope at bright stars like Sirius or Capella when it is found that they do not emit radio waves which are detectable—at least not by our present techniques.

There must be some other explanation of the increase in intensity of the radio waves as the beam of the telescope sweeps across the plane of the galaxy. Our present understanding of the phenomena owes much to the theoretical work of the Russian astrophysicist Shklovsky. We believe that the peak of radio intensity in the region of the galactic plane is made up of two features. First, some radio emission is generated in the hydrogen gas which lies in the plane of the Milky Way system. The hydrogen gas exists in two conditions—neutral hydrogen and ionized hydrogen. The description of the radio emission from neutral hydrogen which occurs on a specific frequency of 1420 Mc/s (wavelength 21 cm.) will be given later in this Chapter.

At the moment we are concerned with the radio waves which originate in the ionized hydrogen gas and which can be received in a radio telescope over a wide range of wavelengths. Stars emit radiation which is absorbed by the hydrogen atoms in their vicinity. The electron in the atom takes a quantum jump away from the proton, and the proton and electron then exist as separate entities—the hydrogen has been ionized. Thus near the hot stars the clouds of hydrogen are fully ionized. When these free electrons pass close to the field of a proton an interaction occurs without the electron being captured by the proton—this is known as a free-free transition and the resultant radiation is emitted on a long wavelength, not as light but in the radio-wave part of the spectrum.

We believe that the radio waves received from the neighbour-hood of the galactic plane at short wavelengths—for example at wavelengths of 10 cm. or so—are generated predominantly by this free-free transition effect. This is commonly known as thermal radiation. On long wavelengths however—in the metre waveband—the peak of intensity near the galactic plane is believed to arise from another process suggested by Shklovsky. The free eletrons in the galaxy move in the galactic magnetic field. There is a well-known principle in physics according to which radiation occurs when electrons are accelerated in a magnetic field. It is known as synchrotron emission, and this appears to be happening in the galaxy on a vast scale, the emission occurring in the radio part of the spectrum. This source of radiation predominates on long radio wavelengths, not only in the galactic plane but also as a halo or corona of radio-wave emission which surrounds and encloses the entire galactic system. In the intermediate range of wavelengths—say 50 cm. to 1 m.—both the thermal and synchrotron emission make significant contributions. The

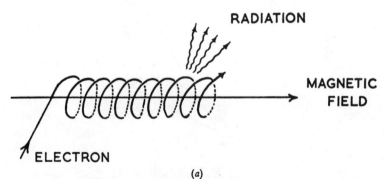

(a)

Fig. 5. Diagrammatic illustration of three forms of radio emission. In (a) an electron is spiralling at very high velocity in the galactic magnetic field. Under the forces of acceleration in these orbits the electron emits radiation known as synchrotron emission.

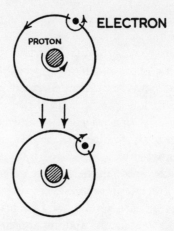

(*b*) The hydrogen line emission on a spectral line at a frequency of 1420.405 Mc/s (21.10 cm.) occurs when the electron spin reverses. There are two possible orientations of the spin direction in the field due to the magnetic moment of the proton, and in the normal state the transition which gives rise to the emission occurs only once in 11,000,000 years.

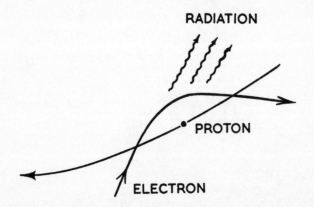

(*c*) Thermal emission from ionized hydrogen occurs when a free electron is accelerated in the field of the proton without capture. This is often known as a ' free-free ' transition.

II. The space probe Pioneer V launched on 11th March 1960. This probe was tracked by the 250-ft. radio telescope at Jodrell Bank daily until early July 1960 when it was at a distance of over 22.5 million miles from Earth. (*By kind permission of Space Technology Laboratories, Los Angeles.*)

III. The 250-ft. radio telescope at Jodrell Bank photographed when a helicopter was removing from the base of the aerial mast inside the bowl the transmitter which was used to command the Pioneer V space probe. (*By kind permission of the Daily Mail.*)

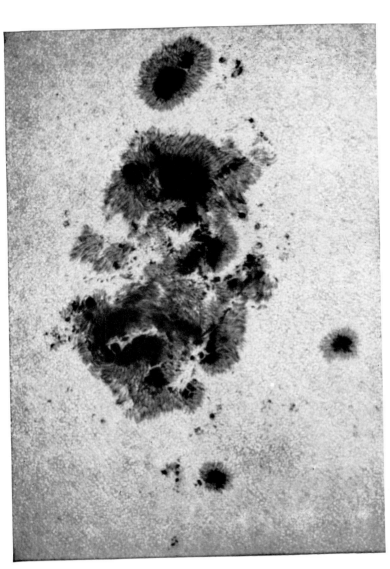

IV. A large group of sunspots photographed on 17 May 1951. Solar flares often erupt in the vicinity of developing sunspots and are associated with powerful radio emission. (*By courtesy of the Mount Wilson and Palomar Observatories.*)

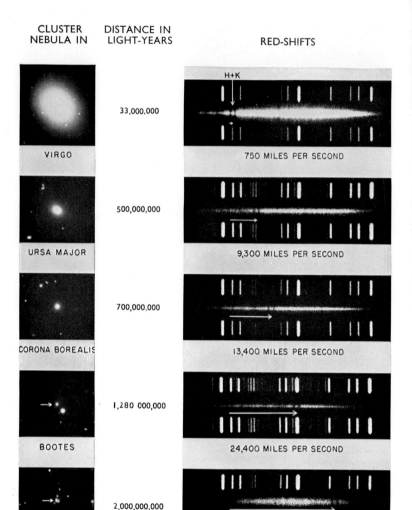

CLUSTER NEBULA IN	DISTANCE IN LIGHT-YEARS	RED-SHIFTS
VIRGO	33,000,000	750 MILES PER SECOND
URSA MAJOR	500,000,000	9,300 MILES PER SECOND
CORONA BOREALIS	700,000,000	13,400 MILES PER SECOND
BOOTES	1,280 000,000	24,400 MILES PER SECOND
HYDRA	2,000,000,000	38,000 MILES PER SECOND

V. The relation between red-shift and distance for extragalactic nebulae. Red-shifts are expressed as apparent velocities of recession, $c\, d\lambda/\lambda$. Arrows indicate the shift of the calcium lines H and K. One light-year is approximately 6 million million miles or 6×10^{12} miles.

(*By courtesy of the Mount Wilson and Palomar Observatories.*)

VI. The 200-inch Hale telescope on Mount Palomar showing the observer in the prime focus cage and the reflecting surface of the 200-inch mirror. (*By courtesy of the Mount Wilson and Palomar Observatories.*)

VII. The Great Spiral Nebula in Andromeda (M31) photographed with the 48-inch Schmidt camera on Mount Palomar.
The galaxy is 2 million light years distant and is just visible to
the naked eye if conditions are good.   The nebula probably
contains 100,000 million stars and is believed to be similar to
the Milky Way system. (*By courtesy of the Mount Wilson and
Palomar Observatories.*)

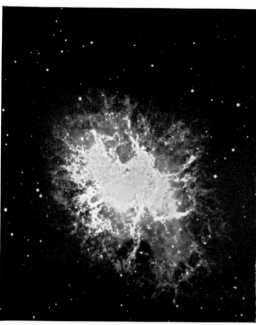

VIII (a) The Lagoon Nebula (M8) in Sagittarius. This nebula is a region of hydrogen gas made luminous by hot stars in the Milky Way. It is believed that new stars may be in process of formation in this and similar nebulae. (*By courtesy of the Mount Wilson and Palomar Observatories.*)

VIII (b) The Crab Nebula—the remains of a supernova explosion which was observed by Chinese astronomers in 1054. The nebula is a powerful source of radio emission in the Galaxy. (*By courtesy of the Mount Wilson and Palomar Observatories.*)

IX. A group of four nebulae in the constellation Leo photographed by the 200-inch Palomar telescope. An elliptical, a spiral, and two barred spiral nebulae can be distinguished. (*By courtesy of the Mount Wilson and Palomar Observatories.*)

detailed analysis of the processes involved and the separation of the components from experimental data, which were far from perfect, was a great triumph for Shklovsky.

In addition to this broadly distributed complex of thermal and synchrotron radio emission, the radio picture of the galaxy is further complicated by the fact that several localized or discrete sources of radio emission are revealed by surveys with the big telescopes. These discrete sources of radio emission remained a puzzle for a long time. Now they are almost all identified and are objects of the most extraordinary interest. The first one to be identified was an object quite close to us, only 4,000 light years away from the solar system, well inside our own galaxy. It is the remains of a star which blew up. The explosion was seen and recorded in the year A.D. 1054 by Chinese astronomers—the famous Crab nebula. In this event the entire material of the star blew up, a tremendous hydrogen bomb explosion involving not just a few pounds of hydrogen but all the trillions of tons of hydrogen comprising the star. When this happens a star which one night is invisible becomes as bright as Venus and then gradually fades away. After a thousand years we now see the remains of the supernova of 1054 as a great streaming gas with the gaseous shell expanding at the rate of about 78 million miles a day.

This object appears to be the third strongest source of radio emission in the sky. It seems likely that the radio emission is generated in this Crab nebula because it has a magnetic field, and the electrons are accelerated to very high energies and emit synchrotron radiation in the radio-wave region of the spectrum in a similar manner to the synchrotron radiation which is emitted in the disc and halo of the galaxy. Substantial support for these ideas has come from the discovery, made in Russia and Leiden, that the light from the nebula is polarized, and also that the radio emission in the short wave centimetre band is polarized. These phenomena are precisely those expected if the magnetic field is playing a prominent part in the processes taking place in the Crab nebula.

Is it possible that the other discrete sources of radio emission are also supernova remnants? Early in the studies of this problem it was realized that there were two classes of discrete sources—a concentration lying in the galactic plane, and another class which appeared to be distributed isotropically over the sky. This isotropically distributed class of discrete sources is now known to lie far beyond the confines of the Milky Way. These radio sources will be discussed in Chapter IV. On the other hand, the sources which, like the Crab nebula, lie in the galactic plane, are undoubtedly objects which are contained within the Milky Way system of stars. The most obvious difficulty of relating these radio sources to supernova remnants is that in the whole of recorded history there are only two other well authenticated cases of supernovae—those observed by Tycho Brahe in 1572 and by Kepler in 1604. The remnants of both have been detected as radio sources and confirm the general picture that supernovae are vigorous emitters of radio waves.

The strongest of all the sources of radio emission in the sky lies in the constellation of Cassiopeia, not obviously related to any prominent visual object. When the radio telescopes had determined the position of this radio source with sufficient accuracy, Baade and Minkowski photographed this region of the sky with the 200-inch Palomar telescope, and they found in the position of the radio source an extremely faint nebulosity containing filaments of gas in violent relative internal motion. They concluded that this object was indeed a supernova remnant not recorded in the astronomical annals.

There is another well known photographic object in the galaxy which is believed to be the expanding gaseous shell of an ancient supernova explosion. This is the famous Cygnus Loop or the veil nebula in Cygnus. If the present velocity of expansion of this shell is projected back in time it fits in with the idea that this is the result of a star which exploded 50,000 years ago. The radio isophotes obtained with a high-definition radio telescope in this region of the sky show a close relation with the filamentary parts of this nebula which are unobscured by dust, and this fact further supports the contention that the discrete sources of radio emission in the galaxy are supernova-like objects.

THE RADIO EMISSION FROM EXTRAGALACTIC NEBULAE

From the photographic evidence it seems that the Milky Way system is typical of many extragalactic spiral nebulae, and in particularly our nearest extragalctic spiral, M31 in Andromeda, seems closely similar to the Milky Way. Does this also apply to the radio emission? The answer is quite straightforward. The individual extragalactic nebulae are generally similar in respect of their total output of radio waves, particularly if the comparison is restricted to those showing the same kind of structure as the

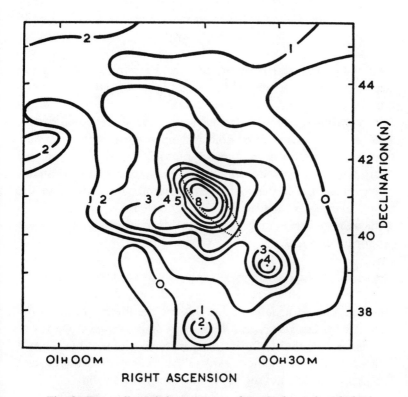

Fig. 6. The radio emission contours of the Andromeda nebula. The dotted region is the outline of the envelope of the nebula visible in the photographs. The radio records show the presence of an extensive radio corona extending to regions of space far outside the aggregate of stars. The numbers on the contours show the relative intensity of the radio emission.

Milky Way or M31. For the structureless elliptical galaxies there is, as yet, no clear indication of radio emission, but these comments are based on a rather small sample of two dozen or so of the nearer nebulae, which is all that our present instruments have succeeded in studying so far.

Even in the case of the nearest of these galaxies, M31, our instruments are not yet sufficiently powerful to show up the existence of discrete or localized sources, but no doubt these exist. On the other hand, the high resolution surveys of M31 show in a very striking manner the corona or halo of radio emission which surrounds the galaxy and underlines the similarity with the Milky Way system. There is evidence, too, that the more distant spirals are similarly enclosed within this corona of radio emission. The discovery of these radio coronae around the galaxies has been one of the most significant additions which radio astronomy has made to the knowledge of our own Milky Way system and of the extragalactic nebulae. The galaxies no longer appear as isolated objects defined by the system of stars which are visible on a photographic plate; they are complex entities, consisting not only of the gas and dust in interstellar space but also of the high-speed electrons accelerating in the galactic magnetic field and producing the corona which envelops the stars in regions of space where no matter is visible in the optical telescopes.

THE RADIO EMISSION FROM THE NEUTRAL HYDROGEN

The hydrogen which is ionized by the stars in the Milky Way system and is partially responsible for the radio emission from the disc of the galaxy, can be seen in photographs of the sky as emission nebulosities. In addition to this ionized hydrogen it seemed only reasonable to assume that the galaxies must contain a great deal of hydrogen in the neutral state, but no direct observational evidence existed for its presence in the Milky Way. Since this hydrogen was neutral there was no means of detecting it optically; for hydrogen to become visible it has to be excited, so that the electrons in it can undergo transitions between different energy levels and thereby emit light, but this was not happening in the vast regions of interstellar space away from the hot stars. However, neutral hydrogen emits radio waves, and thereby hangs one of the most dramatic stories of radio astronomy.

When the Germans were in occupation of Holland the astronomers at Leiden contrived to continue their scientific colloquia under the most extraordinary conditions of difficulty and danger. At one of these colloquia in 1944, van de Hulst, a young astronomer on the staff of Professor Oort at Leiden Observatory, made the suggestion that it ought to be possible to detect the neutral hydrogen in the galaxies because circumstances existed which would cause the hydrogen to emit radio waves on a specific line frequency of 1420 Mc/s—that is on a wavelength of 21 cm. The proton in the hydrogen atom has a magnetic moment; this causes the ground state of the atom to exist in two closely separated energy states, depending on whether the electron is spinning in the same way as the nucleus or in opposition. This is known as the hyperfine structure of the ground state. If the spin of the electron changes its orientation with respect to the nucleus, then the energy of the atom changes by a small amount in this transition. Whereas in the ordinary electron transitions between different energy levels light is emitted, van de Hulst calculated that in this hyperfine transition the energy change was such that the resultant radiation would be emitted on a wavelength of 21 cm. It is difficult now to conceive the boldness of this suggestion, because in another part of van de Hulst's calculation he pointed out that such a transition would be a very rare event and would only happen once in an atom in every 11 million years. Nevertheless, he also said that the concentration of neutral hydrogen in space was so great, there were so many trillions of atoms involved, that in spite of this low probability for the transition, the 21 cm. radio waves emitted in this way should be detectable. Immediately the war ended the astronomers in Leiden set to work to devise some apparatus in an attempt to prove this idea, and simultaneously the radio astronomers in Harvard and Sydney started on the same task. Now this problem is of extraordinary technical difficulty, and it is a remarkable fact that in 1951 all three groups succeeded in measuring this emission on 21 cm. within a few weeks of one another.

The discovery of the 21 cm. emission from the neutral hydrogen gas, and its subsequent exploitation, has been of supreme importance to astronomy. Not only have the radio telescopes penetrated to the gas clouds which are obscured by the dust between us and the central region of the galaxy but they have measured with precision the spiral nature of the Milky Way. This has been possible because in this transition the radio wave is emitted on a specific frequency of 1420 Mc/s. If the atoms are moving with respect to the observer then a doppler effect can be observed. The measured frequency differs from the emitted frequency of 1420 Mc/s in direct proportion to the relative speed of movement of the gas clouds and the observer, in an analogous manner to the change in pitch of a train whistle as it moves out of a station. In the latter case we are dealing with sound waves and the change in pitch is due to the relative motion of the train and the observer. In the case of the hydrogen atoms we are dealing with radio waves, and the change in the measured frequency arises because the hydrogen atoms in the gas clouds are in motion with respect to the solar system, and hence with respect to the observer on earth. Fundamentally, the emitted radio waves remain precisely on the calculated frequency of 1420.40 Mc/s; therefore, if the actual frequency at which they are received on earth is determined, we can find out how fast and in what direction these hydrogen clouds are moving with respect to the solar system.

By systematic observations of this type the astronomers in Leiden and Sydney have studied the hydrogen clouds in the galaxy and have succeeded in determining their motion with respect to us. The results of this work show the spiral formation of the galaxy with great clarity and confirm beyond doubt the similarity of the large-scale structure of the Milky Way system to the extragalactic spiral nebulae.

The nucleus of the galaxy is so heavily obscured optically that it is only now becoming available for investigation by virtue of the hydrogen line emission. Until recently our knowledge of the conditions near the central regions of galaxies has come mainly from the investigation of the extragalactic nebula M31. In the early photographs with the 100-inch telescope the stars could clearly be seen in the spiral arms, but nevertheless in the central regions no stars could be seen. For a long time, it was believed that the central regions of the galaxy represented an amorphous mass of material where there were no stars. During the war Baade took advantage of the fact that Los Angeles was blacked out and used the 100-inch Mount Wilson telescope to photograph the nucleus of the Andromeda nebula with red sensitive plates. He found that this nuclear region was far from being amorphous; that it was very clearly resolved into stars, but stars of a different type from those which had been commonly photographed in the spiral arms of the galaxy. The stars in the spiral arms are predominantly blue, but those which Baade photographed in the nuclear region of the M31 galaxy turned out to be red. They were red giants and he called them population II. Now it is common to talk of population I and population II. The population I stars are those in the spiral arms, the blue stars in the process of formation; the population II stars are, on the whole, the red giants which are in the nuclear regions of these galactic systems. They are old stars, existing in regions where star formation has largely ceased. Compared with the spiral arms of the galaxies the relative amount of hydrogen gas to stars in the central regions is extremely low. For example, Oort has estimated that within 30 light years of the galactic centre, the density of material in the Milky Way system is 24,000 times greater than the density near the sun—but this density is almost entirely due to the great concentration of stars in this nuclear region. Even within 1,500 light years of the centre, Oort estimates that the hydrogen gas contributes only $\frac{1}{400}$ of the total mass. This has to be compared with the situation in the spiral arms near the vicinity of the solar system 25,000 light years from the centre, where the interstellar gas contributes $\frac{1}{2}$ of the total mass.

Recently the Leiden astronomers have made a remarkable discovery about the gas in these central regions. At a distance of 6,000 light years from the central region there seems to be a

dense arm which is taking part in the rotation of the galactic
system with a velocity of 200 km./sec. The unexpected feature of
these observations is that the hydrogen gas in this arm appears
to be moving radially away from the centre with a velocity of
more than 50 km./sec. At this rate of streaming the central
regions would become entirely devoid of gas in a time of about
one thousand million or at the most two thousand million years.
How is this gas being replenished? Perhaps from the galactic
corona, but we do not know for certain. The Russian astronomer,
Ambartsumian, has even suggested that it may be produced from
matter in some entirely unknown state. Both the reason for the
expansion and the mode of replenishment is one of the interesting contemporary problems in astronomy.

THE PROCESSES OF STAR FORMATION

The two major influences on our present beliefs about the
processes of star formation have been the understanding of the
hydrogen-to-helium conversion as the source of stellar energy,
and the recognition of the existence of distinct classes of stars—
the population I and population II. The population II stars
appear to be the fundamental and ancient stars in the universe.
They are found in the nuclear regions of the galaxies, in the
globular clusters and in the elliptical galaxies—and in these
regions there is comparatively little of the interstellar hydrogen
gas remaining. By contrast, the population I stars seem to be a
comparatively recent phenomenon in the universe. They are in
evidence wherever the concentrations of hydrogen gas exist—
particularly in the spiral arms of the galaxies, and it is in these
regions that we must search for evidence of the processes of star
formation.

Indeed, in the extensive bright nebulous clouds of hydrogen
gas which exist in the spiral arms certain small dark objects—
the galactic globules—may well represent the early stages of star
formation. These globules are circular and small—only a light
year or less in diameter—and studies of their opacity indicate
that the masses of the globules may be of the same order as that
of the sun. These globules are probably clouds in the process of

condensation under the influence of the radiation pressure from the surrounding stars and perhaps here, before our eyes, we have evidence of the stars in process of formation.

The processes may develop in this way. A slight disturbance in the huge amorphous mass of hydrogen gas may initiate the beginning of the condensation of the globules which proceeds under the influence of the self-gravitation of the mass of gas in the globule, assisted by the radiation pressure of the surrounding starlight. From these initial processes the building up of a gigantic globule of rarefied gas might take a hundred million years. As the contraction continues, more and more of the potential gravitational energy of the mass of gas is liberated; the temperature of the globule will rise so that the condensate will begin to radiate —first in the infra-red and then in the visible part of the spectrum. Eventually the central regions of this condensing mass begin to get so hot that thermonuclear reactions will occur. Probably when the temperature is half a million degrees nuclear processes involving protons and deuterium will occur. At this stage the contraction of the star will be halted, but when the deuterium is exhausted contraction will recommence and the central temperature will again rise until at a few million degrees other light elements will begin to take part in the nuclear processes.

Eventually, after these preliminary stages, the condition will be reached when the conversion of hydrogen to helium begins in the carbon-nitrogen cycle. After a few tens of millions of years the main supply of hydrogen in the star will begin to be exhausted and the energy production which has hitherto prevented the contraction of the star begins to fail, so that ultimately the star collapses into a white dwarf. Then the central pressure reaches such enormous values that the conventional atomic structure collapses and the matter becomes degenerate.

Our own sun is well established in the hydrogen-helium conversion phase as described in Chapter II. The initial globule of the star which is now our sun probably began to form in the primeval hydrogen gas over ten thousand million years ago, and half of the original hydrogen has already been exhausted. It seems to be a typical case of a star in the middle of the main sequence. The sun can continue to burn up its remaining hydrogen and remain in an equilibrium state for about another five or six thousand million years. But then all the reserves of its hydrogen will begin to be exhausted and there can be no further production of energy by thermonuclear processes to balance the gravitational forces which are tending to pull the remaining gas together. At that time the sun will begin to collapse, but then the pressure will build up to such an extent that even more energy will be generated and it will then begin to expand. For the subsequent million years while its thermonuclear processes are ceasing, any civilizations which still exist in the solar system would vanish quickly because the conditions would change so rapidly. First of all the temperature of the earth would begin to increase at a rate of about 10° every million years, so that eventually all the oceans would boil and the sun itself would become so inflated that it would occupy most of the space of the solar system. But then at that stage all its reserves of energy will finally disappear, there will be nothing further left which is capable of transformation to produce energy, and the final collapse will take place leading to the condition of a white dwarf.

This picture of the probable trend of evolution of the stars is of course a very simplified one. In some cases catastrophes happen which give rise to supernova like the Crab nebula. In this case the heavy elements which have already been formed in a star are ejected into space and are probably absorbed in the interstellar clouds where new stars are beginning to form. The interstellar hydrogen contains the scatterings of heavy elements from stars which long ago ended their lives in a supernova explosion. This seems to be the explanation of the presence on earth and in the planetary system of the heavy elements which could not possibly have been formed by the sun itself in its present stage.

In the central regions of the galaxy, where the population II stars predominate, there is no evidence of star formation taking place; the hydrogen has vanished and the stars are old. The reasons for this are not really understood; it is a subject which belongs to the evolution of the galaxies themselves and of the cosmos as a whole. It seems that when our own Milky Way system, M31, and the other galaxies were formed the processes of star formation in the central regions of the galaxies took place first of all. Either this used up all the gas in the early history of the galaxy, or some other collisions took place which swept the remaining gas away from these central regions. In any case, today it is only in the spiral arms of the galaxies, where we still have these regions of hydrogen gas, that stars are being born.

IV

THE ORIGIN AND EVOLUTION
OF THE UNIVERSE

THE cosmological problem is epitomized by many typical photographs taken by the large optical telescopes in which it is possible to distinguish almost as many extragalactic nebulae as there are foreground stars in the Milky Way. Where-ever one looks in space there seem to be these great numbers of galaxies. Many of these galaxies are similar to the Milky Way and must contain something like 10,000 million to 100,000 million stars of which our sun might be a typical member. On the whole, these galaxies seem to be uniformly distributed throughout the observable universe—at least when the large-scale distribution is considered. The optical telescopes can penetrate to about 5,000 million light years, and within this region of space and time the universe does not seem to be markedly different from what it is today, as indicated by the photographs and the arrangement of the galaxies in the space around our own Milky Way system.

There are indeed indications of a certain structure in the cosmos because few of these galaxies exist on their own; they are nearly all contained in clusters or groups. The Milky Way system belongs to a small group of galaxies which includes the Andromeda nebula, M31, our closest neighbour, at a distance of 2 million light years, and about a dozen others. This group occupies a volume of space in the shape of a flattened ellipsoid with a major axis of two million light years, a minor axis of a million light years, and a thickness of about 500,000 light years. Our own galaxy is near the extremity of this group, about a million light years from the centre which lies in the direction of the Andromeda nebula. Compared with some of the clusters which can be photographed this is, indeed, a small group. For example, the cluster of galaxies in Virgo is about 14 million light years distant from us; it extends for at least 2 or 3 million light years and contains several hundred galaxies.

In the Coma cluster of galaxies, which is 90 million light years distant, it is possible to describe an area of sky no bigger than that occupied by the full moon, in which something like 500 galaxies are concentrated. These figures serve to indicate the enormous quantity of material which we have to deal with in the universe and the vastness of the problem. The galaxies contained within the field of view of the 200-inch telescope are effectively uncountable; all that can be said is that down to 22nd and 23rd magnitude, which is near the limit of visibility of the telescope, it has been estimated that there are something of the order of a million trillion galaxies.

There is one quite remarkable feature of the observations of these extragalactic nebulae which presents a critical problem in respect of any attempted explanation of the origin of the universe and, indeed, of its future history. This observation is that the spectral lines in the light from the distant galaxies are shifted towards the red end of the spectrum. The first critical measurements were made in 1912 at the Lowell Observatory by Slipher, who found that if the shift were interpreted in the conventional way as a doppler displacement, then the indicated velocities of recession were much greater than for any other known celestial object. The real significance of these measurements was not apparent until Hubble in the period 1922-24 gave conclusive arguments in support of the concept that the nebulae were extragalactic lying far beyond the confines of the Milky Way, and then in 1929 announced that the red-shift seemed to be linearly related to the distance of the galaxy. This implies that the velocity of recession of the extragalactic nebulae increases as their distance from us increases. The most tremendous arguments have taken place about the interpretation of this reddening, but now all astronomers agree to an explanation which implies that this reddening is due to a doppler shift, indicating that the galaxies are moving apart at a great speed.

Some of these early measurements were surprising enough. For example, the well known Virgo cluster of galaxies at a

distance of 7 million light years showed a red-shift which
indicated a velocity of 600 miles per second; but with the advent
of the 200-inch telescope, the limits of penetration were extended
to such a degree that the indicated speeds of recession reached
appreciable fractions of the velocity of light. In 1960 the most
distant cluster yet identified in Boötes 5,000 million light years
away, showed a recessional velocity of 46 per cent. of the velocity
of light—86,000 miles per second. It is a fact, difficult to com-
prehend, that during the time taken to read a few lines of this
print we have separated by another million miles from the
objects which we can photograph at the extreme limits of our
penetration into the universe. The entire universe is expanding
at an enormous rate, and there is not yet any reliable evidence
which indicates a departure from linear relationship between
velocity of recession and distance, at least out to several thousand
million light years. Any theory of the universe has to explain not
only the existence of this recession of the nebulae but also the
fact that it increases linearly with distance out to the furthest
limit of penetration of the big telescopes.

In spite of this dramatic revelation of the content, arrangement, and movement of the galaxies in space, the optical
telescopes have failed to show any differences in the large-scale
organization of the universe out to these distances. In other
words, the telescopes have failed so far to reveal any changes in
the past history of the universe. The critical point in this
argument is that as we look out into space, so we look back in
time, because the light from these distant objects has been
thousands of millions of years on its journey to us. We are,
therefore, studying the universe as it existed thousands of millions
of years ago in time past. Therefore one can say from the
observations with the optical telescopes that back to an epoch
of a few thousand million years there do not appear to have
been any great changes in the organization of the cosmos.

THE IMPACT OF RADIO ASTRONOMY ON COSMOLOGY

The advent of the radio telescopes quite unexpectedly introduced a dramatic new situation into cosmological studies. The

general features of the radio map of the heavens have already been described in Chapter III: that the radio emission from the Milky Way can be explained in terms of the radiation from hydrogen gas, and from certain discrete sources concentrated in the plane of the Milky Way which are identified with supernova remnants. The radio observations with a high-definition radio telescope also reveal thousands of discrete sources of radio waves having a distribution which is nearly isotropic and only a few of these can be linked up with the individual extragalactic nebulae which are fairly close to us in space, such as M31.

The first suggestion that these radio sources might be of cosmological significance arose when an attempt was made to identify the second strongest source of radio emission in the sky —in the constellation of Cygnus. Nature confused the issue because this source, like the slightly stronger one in Cassiopeia, was close to the galactic plane. As we have seen, the Cassiopeia source was identified with a supernova remnant in the galaxy, but there was no galactic object possessing any features which might have been responsible for the intense source in Cygnus. In fact, the region of the sky in question was rather undistinguished; it contained many faint distant stars in the Milky Way system, but nothing which would indicate that there could be an object responsible for such strong radio emission.

After some years of this dilemma the position of the Cygnus radio source was measured with sufficient accuracy to enable Baade and Minkowski to use the 200-inch telescope on Mount Palomar and make a very long exposure of this region of the sky. In their series of photographs of this region Baade and Minkowski discovered an unusual object which they identified as two spiral galaxies closely interacting. The possibility that galaxies might, under certain conditions, collide with one another had given rise to some speculation before the advent of radio astronomy. It seemed possible that in the very dense clusters the galaxies must be close enough together, and, since they are moving at random under their own gravitational attraction, then some at least must occasionally run into one another. No such cases were discovered until this example of strong radio emission led to the photography of this region of the sky.

There were immediately two important consequences. First, the object was estimated to be at a very great distance—700 million light years away. Second, although the object was extremely faint optically, the output of energy in the radio wave region was considerable, to such an extent that it was the second strongest source of radio emission known. This interpretation of the phenomenon has turned out to be of the utmost significance to cosmology because it appears that under certain circumstances events take place in the universe which give rise to a relatively large output of energy in the radio wave part of the spectrum, although optically the objects themselves are very faint. Indeed, if these colliding galaxies in Cygnus, which are at 700 million light years, were ten times further away, that is at 7,000 million light years, then it would be impossible to photograph them with any of the world's optical telescopes; but the radio telescopes would still record the interacting galaxies as a prominent object. This conception led to the idea that the difficulty of relating many of these radio sources to objects which can be photographed might be that they existed as cases of collisions of galaxies so far away in the cosmos that they were beyond the range of the world's biggest optical telescope. This is indeed what we now believe to be the case. The problem is of great significance because we hope that these radio studies will enable us to penetrate to those regions of space and time which lie beyond the photographic limit, where it may be possible to discover signs of change in the past history of the universe.

It should be mentioned that the interpretation of the Cygnus photograph as an example of two galaxies in collision is not unanimously accepted amongst astronomers. In particular, the Russian astronomer Ambartsumian takes the view that the object is an example of the division of the nucleus of a galaxy to form two separate galaxies. In any case, both in this example and in the others subsequently discovered, the crucial observation for cosmology is that certain processes can take place in distant, faint photographic objects which produce a relatively large output of energy in the radio-wave part of the spectrum.

THE INVESTIGATION OF THE DISTANT RADIO SOURCES

Large-scale investigations of these sources of radio waves at very great distances are in progress, and special telescopes have been developed for this work. One frequently used technique is the employment of a radio telescope which effectively consists of two aerials, separated, perhaps, by many miles. Then instead of the single beam of the parabolic reflector, the reception pattern of the combined aerials is a system of lobes. As the earth sweeps this beam across the sky, a source of radio waves of angular diameter, large compared with the separation of the lobes, gives a smooth pattern. On the other hand, if the radio waves came from a source whose angular extent is small compared with the separation between the lobes, then the received pattern will show maxima and minima as the earth sweeps the lobe pattern across the source.

By using this and similar techniques, Ryle at Cambridge and the radio astronomers in Sydney, Australia, have investigated the distribution of several thousand of these radio sources. If the objects in the universe are distributed uniformly in space and time then, because the radio intensity or optical intensity will decrease as the inverse square of the distance, there will be a definite relation between the number of objects and their brightness (in the radio or optical sense). In fact it is not difficult to calculate that if the logarithm of the number of objects of a given brightness is plotted against the logarithm of the intensity, then the result should be a straight line with a slope of 1.5.

The radio astronomers have plotted their results in this form to show how the number of radio sources increases as the intensity diminishes, and it is to be expected that, if the distribution were uniform in space and time, then the relation would be a straight line with this slope of 1.5. In fact, the Cambridge observations indicate that although there is good agreement with this uniform spatial distribution for the strong radio sources, the agreement disappears as one gets to fainter and fainter sources. There is a departure of the experimental curve from the theoretical straight line, the departure being in the sense which indicates that for very weak radio sources (which

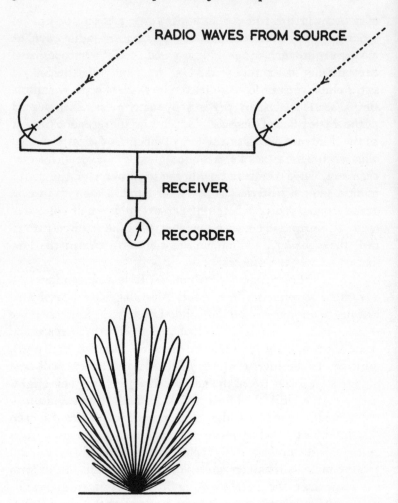

Fig. 7. A simple two-aerial interferometer with resultant polar
diagram showing the family of lobes.

are presumably at great distances) the numbers appear to be
greater than would be indicated by the concept of a uniform
distribution in space and time. If we take the simplest interpretation of this result, the conclusion is inevitable that the content
of the universe—the spatial density of the material, the number

of galaxies or the number of radio sources per unit volume of space—is greater in those remote parts than in the regions closer to us in space and time. If this result could be substantiated beyond doubt then it would be of the greatest cosmological significance, because for the first time we would have an indication of some change in the organization of the cosmos as we penetrate further into space and further back into time. Of course this result from the counting of the radio sources is exactly what one might expect if the universe were in an evolving state, because as we look back to these regions of time, many thousand million years ago, we would expect to find a universe more densely populated and nearer the point of its origin than it is today. Unfortunately, and perhaps because of the significance of the conclusions, this work has been severely criticized. The derivation of the statistics is a complicated process and, moreover, a similar experiment by the workers in Sydney has yielded a contrary result, indicating that there is no departure from the uniform distribution out to the limits of penetration of the radio telescopes.

An attempt to overcome this dilemma, and to evade the criticism that one could not treat the radio source counts in this statistical manner, has been made at Jodrell Bank. The problem has, in fact, occupied more than a third of the working time of the radio telescope in the first four years of its use, which means that 5,000 or 6,000 hours of work have been spent on this aspect of the cosmological problem. In this system the telescope at Jodrell Bank is used in conjunction with smaller aerials which can be moved to different distances from it. The greatest separation so far achieved is 72 miles. The information from these remote stations is transmitted over a radio link and is correlated with the signals picked up simultaneously in the radio telescope at Jodrell Bank. The aim of this experiment is to measure the strength of the radio waves and the apparent angular diameter of the sources. With this information we would know much more about the distant radio sources because we could calculate the effective temperature of the source and begin to get some scale of distance for these unidentified sources. The experiment is carried out by changing the spacing of the distant aerial until the lobe separation becomes so small that the maximum and minimum in the interferometer fringe pattern of a particular source begins to disappear. The source is then beginning to be resolved, and it is possible to estimate the actual angular diameter of the emitting region.

So far, out of 300 of the most intense unidentified radio sources which we believe to be at distances of cosmical significance, only about 10 per cent. of them have angular diameters which would indicate that they were at distances greater than about 2,000 million light years. Of these, three have proved quite remarkable in that at the greatest spacing of the aerials the intensity of the fringes has remained unchanged, indicating that the radio sources must have angular diameters less than a second of arc. The interpretation to be placed on this result, based on the known distance and characteristics of the Cygnus source, is that these sources must be situated so far away in the universe that the radio waves have been on their journey for probably 7,000 or 8,000 million years.

The import of the radio investigations has been made manifest by the successful optical identification in 1960 of one of these sources of small angular diameter. The actual co-ordinates of this radio source had been very well determined and its characteristics indicated that it was typical of a Cygnus-type object— that is, where galaxies are in collision or closely interacting. The result of the investigation of the appropriate region of the sky by the 200-inch Palomar telescope was that the radio source was related to a cluster of galaxies in the constellation of Boötes. This cluster of galaxies in Boötes represents at present the greatest distance to which the Palomar telescope has penetrated— 5,000 million light years—with a speed of recession, as measured by the red-shift, of 46 per cent. of the velocity of light or 86,000 miles per second. An interesting consequence of this co-operation between the radio telescopes and the optical telescopes has been that within a few years the ultimate range of the 200-inch optical telescope on Palomar has increased by a factor of 3.

The results at the moment are consistent with the belief that many of these unidentified radio sources are cases of dense clusters of galaxies, extremely far away in time and space. For reasons which are not really understood, but which are almost certainly associated with the interaction of the dust and gas in the galaxies during the collisions, they generate relatively intense radio waves although their output of energy in the optical part of the spectrum is rather small. At the moment, in the region of space out to the 2,000 million light year cluster in Hydra, apart from this new one in Boötes, there are about a dozen of these peculiar nebulae which have been identified. Although there can be little doubt that the radio observations of the un-identified sources have great importance in cosmology, it will probably take many years of work before the results can be used to make firm cosmological predictions.

THEORIES OF THE COSMOS

We must now consider what these observations may mean in terms of our ideas about the evolution and origin of the cosmos. Cosmology was given a new impetus with the development of Einstein's theory of general relativity because the solutions of the equations of general relativity appeared to have an import-ant bearing on the arrangement of matter in space. In the solu-tion of these equations there is an arbitrary constant—the lambda term or the cosmic constant. The problem of the value to be attached to this cosmical constant has caused extensive contro-versies in cosmology over the past few decades because there are a variety of model universes which can be specified by the equa-tions of general relativity depending on this constant. Not all of the possible models have been explored theoretically but they all have this in common : they represent a universe in some kind of evolutionary state ; a universe which in time past had some degree of singularity. A universe which has this unique or singular condition in a past epoch presents many associated problems—particularly with regard to the problem of creation at a specific time.

During the last ten years Hoyle, Bondi, Gold, and McCrea have brought forward an entirely new theory of cosmology which uses the equations of general relativity in which the cosmcial constant is made zero—the theory of continuous creation or the steady state theory. On this theory the universe has never had any singularity in the past, neither will it in the future. They invoke the perfect cosmological principle in which the universe is the same through all space *and time*, so that however far we go back into the past and however far into the future we will always find the same kind of universe as we find today. In order to maintain this stable situation in face of the obvious expansion of the universe the concept implies that the primeval material of the universe, the hydrogen atoms, are being created now, at this moment, continuously, at such a rate that they form into galaxies to make up for those that are moving out of our field of view.

Today the cosmological situation is one of extreme interest and complexity. The evolutionary and the steady state theories are in sharp contrast, and although there are many variations of the evolutionary theories, they all imply an origin of the universe, or a singular condition, in some finite and predictable past epoch. This contrast between the predictions of the evolutionary and steady state theories in time past should make it possible to devise a specific observational test to distinguish between them. Indeed we think now that the radio records which give us information about the state of the universe at distances of 7,000 or 8,000 million light years must refer to a region of space and time where the differences between these two theories should be manifest.

The concept of the unchanging nature of the universe in time and space of the steady state theory, carries the implication that however far we recede into time past the large-scale appearance of the universe will be the same as it is today. The primeval hydrogen atoms are being created at the rate of about one atom per cubic mile of space per year, but this means that trillions of tons are being created every second in the observable universe. This creation of hydrogen has two consequences on the steady state theories. First, it provides the necessary material for the galaxies to form at just the right rate to compensate for those which are moving out of our field of view because of the expansion of the universe; and second, it is the pressure arising from the creation of this material which provides the driving force resulting in the expansion of the universe.

In principle there is a simple observational test between the evolutionary and the steady state theories, because if we can penetrate far enough back into past time then on the steady state theory we should find exactly the same number of galaxies per unit volume of space as we do in our local neighbourhood, whereas on the evolutionary theory the predictions are quite different. The spatial density of galaxies will not be the same as in the regions of time and space closer to us. Indeed it is obvious that if the universe did in fact originate from a superdense initial state in an epoch 10,000 million years ago, then in the regions of space some 7,000 million light years distant to which we believe the radio telescopes are penetrating, the spatial density of galaxies will be much greater than they are today. The optical telescopes have not so far penetrated to regions where any marked differences are apparent, but it is in these regions more than 5,000 million light years distant where there is reason to hope that the classification of the radio sources may show whether the spatial density of the galaxies is varying as we penetrate into time past.

THE MODEL UNIVERSES IN EVOLUTIONARY COSMOLOGY

If the steady state theory is correct then the universe has never had a beginning and will never have an end, and it is useless to ask when time and space began or when time and space will end because the question is meaningless within the framework of the theory of continuous creation. On the other hand, the situation in the evolutionary theories is completely different because they do accept the possibility of a singular condition of the universe, and the creation of matter in time present has no part in the theories. The essence of the evolutionary ideas can be appreciated if we imagine the recession of the galaxies reversed. We are separating from the cluster of galaxies in Boötes with a speed of nearly half the velocity of light—86,000 miles a second. Therefore a few minutes ago we were millions of miles closer to this cluster than we are now. If we retrace the history of the cosmos in this way we find that about 10,000 million years ago all the material which now forms the galaxies must have been closely packed together. On at least some of the evolutionary models this moment must represent the beginning of the universe, the beginning of time and space. Because of the possible variations in the value of the cosmical constant, the various evolutionary models differ considerably in their description of the cosmos at this epoch.

For example, one model which has had considerable vogue is due to Gamov. In this model it is assumed that 10,000 million years ago the whole material of the universe was indeed contained in a primeval lump of material of fundamental particles—probably neutrons and protons. At the beginning of time this supercondensate exploded, and on Gamov's theory all the elements which we know today were formed within the first few hours of the history of the universe. Actually a situation in which all the elements were formed in this way seems impossible because certain light elements required in the sequence are not stable. On the other hand we believe now that element formation is taking place in the hot central cores of the stars and this criticism of the theory may not therefore be serious. On this theory of Gamov's the origin of the universe occurred 10,000 million years ago, the cosmical constant is zero, and the expansion which we witness today is simply the result of the impetus of this initial explosion.

One of the most thoroughly studied evolutionary models is that of the Abbé Lemaître. His theory also implies that the galaxies began to form at this period of about 10,000 million years ago. But in his view the cosmical constant in Einstein's equation is positive, it has a real meaning, and he does not believe that the expansion of the universe which we see today is the result of the impetus of the initial explosion. In fact, to get to the beginning of the Lemaître universe we have to retrace our steps, not for 10,000 million years but for a period of time which is not exactly defined but is probably between 40,000 and 60,000 million years in the past. At that time, according to Lemaître, the universe was in its original state of the primeval atom. Lemaître's primeval atom must have been a concentrate of neutrons or protons so closely packed that the actual nuclei of the atoms were squashed against one another in a completely degenerate state. This primeval atom must have contained the entire mass of the universe which we see around us today; 10^{21} tons in a volume of space no bigger than the solar system is today. The density in this primeval lump must have been colossal, something like a million million times the density of water.

Such a condensate would obviously be in a most unstable condition and at this moment of time the primeval atom must have suffered some radioactive disintegration and the material began to spread out into space. After a thousand million years of time, space, according to the Lemaître theory, occupied about a thousand million light years and was full of hydrogen gas uniformly distributed. At this stage it seemed possible that the universe might settle down into a steady condition. Indeed such a condition was the starting point of Eddington's theory of the universe in which there was a uniform distribution of hydrogen atoms spread through a region of space of about a thousand million light years in diameter.

After this period of a thousand million years the initial impetus of the decay of the primeval atom was exhausted and the gravitational forces had introduced a state of stability. Then condensations in the gas began to occur. The positive cosmical constant in Lemaître's equation is equivalent to a physical force which works in opposition to the Newtonian forces of gravitation, and so on the cosmical scale we have a repulsion which works in opposition to the forces of attraction. Hence when the condensations formed in the gaseous mass the universe began on its career of expansion which we witness today. The time at which the galaxies began to form from the gaseous condensations is not exactly defined by the theory. Neither does Lemaître's equation lead to predictions about the time of appearance of the population II stars in the nuclei of the galaxies, or of the relation between the formation of those stars and the initial formation of the galaxies. The present belief that the main formation of the population II stars occurred 8,000 or 9,000 million years ago, and that population I stars are still in process of formation, is not at variance with the main features of Lemaître's theory. Indeed it is extraordinarily difficult to find any single observational feature, either in terms of the ages of the galaxies or of the formation of stars, which would be completely decisive evidence for or against these various cosmological theories.

In another variant of the evolutionary theory, with a different arrangement of the constants, the universe has a hyperbolic form. After a certain degree of expansion it begins to contract again and the process of expansion and contraction is cyclic, and capable of indefinite repetition.

As far as the future history of the cosmos is concerned, continuous creation leads to the concept of an infinite future existence. The end of the universe has no meaning. Although M31 and the other galaxies will disappear from the region accessible to our telescopes, nevertheless other galaxies will form from the newly created hydrogen atoms, and the universe is ageless. On the evolutionary theories a singularity occurred when all the material must have been created at once and no further creation has been taking place since that time. Therefore, the future outlook for the universe is bleak, because the material is dispersing and the universe will die. This is the essence of the conflicts in cosmology today which we are seeking to clarify by the observations with the radio telescopes. At least we are optimistic enough to believe that the radio telescopes will penetrate to those regions of time and space where the differences between the cosmologies should become apparent.

The bearing of the theories of cosmology on philosophy and theology is often discussed, and indeed the subject is one of extreme interest and importance. It has frequently been said that the steady state theory is entirely a materialistic theory because it does not involve any moment when a unique act of creation could have taken place, and moreover all the tenets of the theory are effectively open to observational test. On the other hand, it has been claimed that the evolutionary theories are entirely in accordance with theological doctrine in that they invoke a moment of singularity which might involve a unique act of creation in time past. My personal attitude is that neither theory necessarily possesses these attributes. There is a fundamental principle in physics which implies that it is impossible to observe any event with precision—the uncertainty principle. For the steady state theory to be proved materialistic, one would have to be able to imagine the development of a perfect scientific instrument which could, in principle, observe the creation of a single atom of the hydrogen which the theory predicts to be taking place continuously. Even if one could devise such an instrument then one would still never be able to obtain any exact knowledge of the creation of the hydrogen atom because in the very act of observing it the uncertainty principle implies that one would disturb it, and therefore one could never obtain any exact information about the basic process of creation.

The evolutionary theories envisage a moment in the remote past when all matter was created. Again for fundamental reasons, in which the finite velocity of light is involved, one can never observe this epoch. At 5,000 million light years we are already dealing with an object which is receding from us at a speed nearly half the velocity of light, and this velocity of recession is still increasing linearly with distance. Any material which exists near the time of the singularity must be receding with a speed which is closely approaching the velocity of light, and therefore can never be observable. Hence any precise observational knowledge of this critical past epoch is forever forbidden to us. Eddington epitomized the problem when he said that light is like a runner on a track which is ever expanding so that the winning post is always receding from him faster than he can run. This is exactly the situation as far as we are concerned with the observation of the remotest parts of space and time which would contain the singularities on any of the evolutionary theories.

Although with our telescopes we shall no doubt clarify the cosmological problem to a large extent, the ultimate issue of the origin of the cosmos may well be a metaphysical one lying outside the realms which the tools of physics and astronomy can approach for reasons which are inherent in fundamental scientific theory.

V

SOME REFLECTIONS ON ETHICS
AND THE COSMOS

OR the past few years I have used a small amount of the
operational time of the radio telescope at Jodrell Bank to
study some characteristics of a group of stars which by
cosmical standards are rather close to us in space. When my
experiment had already been going for some time I was surprised
to receive a letter signed by an American scientist urging me to
use the telescope to search for signals such as might be radiated
by intelligent beings in space. I was even more surprised to read
the suggestion that the most likely chance of success was to
study the stars which were already interesting me in my own
experiment.

I did not react to this request, because I could not reasonably
divert the telescope, which was in great demand, to a speculative
programme. A group of American radio astronomers had more
faith and carried out a search along the lines suggested. As far as
I know the results of this search have been negative. Although I
would find it difficult to justify the diversion of any of the world's
present radio telescopes to such speculative work, nevertheless
during the last two years or so the discussion of the general
problem of the existence of extraterrestrial life appears to have
become both respectable and important.

The respectability has arisen because contemporary scientific
ideas make it seem less likely that the evolution of the solar
system and life in it was unique. The importance arises because
of the critical state which world civilization has reached and the
possibility that civilizations elsewhere have either passed through
this phase of evolution successfully or extinguished themselves at
the stage which we have now reached.

THE FORMATION OF PLANETARY SYSTEMS

A few decades ago it was fashionable to believe in the uniqueness of the solar system. The basic scientific concept was that in the past a star approached close enough to another star (which is now our sun) to raise great tides and pull out from it streams of stellar material. The wandering star continued on its journey through space. The ejected material was captured by the sun and after aeons of time condensed to form the earth and the planetary system.

There were two significant corollaries. The close approach of two stars in this way must be a very rare occurrence and in spite of the hundred thousand million stars of the Milky Way it seemed extremely unlikely that other similar planetary systems could exist elsewhere in the universe. The second corollary was that the earth and the planets condensed initially in a molten state and that therefore the evolution of organic material on earth must have occurred locally after the cooling of the earth's surface.

The development of astronomical theory in the last twenty years has made it quite clear that this type of accidental encounter idea as a basis for the origin of the solar system cannot be sustained. There is no unanimous view as to the precise mode of formation of the system but the current beliefs all have important corollaries concerning the multiplicity of planetary systems in the universe. It seems likely that several thousand million years ago the sun was surrounded by a nebula of gas and dust and that the earth and planets were formed through the successive aggregation into larger and larger bodies from the material of the nebula. This leads to the significant corollary that the earth and planets were formed in a cold state and hence any primeval organisms which might have existed on the dust of the nebula could have survived these formative processes. There are various views as to the process by which the sun collected this nebula. For example it might have collected the dust and gas as it passed through one of the great clouds which pervade interstellar space. Or it might have collected the nebula as part of the debris of the cloud of primeval material which formed many thousands of stars. In either case the important consequence is that many stars in the Milky Way must have similar nebulae associated with them, and hence planetary systems amongst the hundred thousand million stars of the Milky Way must be of frequent occurrence. Amongst the trillions of galaxies similar to the Milky Way in the observable universe there must be vast numbers of planetary systems similar to that which we ourselves inhabit.

THE POSSIBILITIES OF EXTRATERRESTRIAL LIFE

Most of us who have been brought up in the traditional manner of the first half of this century and have absorbed the conventional interpretation of theological doctrines and of astronomical theory have usually accepted as axiomatic that human life on earth was unique. Now we are faced with an entirely different situation. We believe that the solar system, far from being the sole example of its kind in the cosmos, is probably paralleled by planetary systems around stars which are of extremely frequent occurrence in space. This conclusion is very generally accepted today. On the possibility that life exists elsewhere in the cosmos one must therefore ask two questions. First, how many of these planetary systems are in conditions of stability with parent stars not dissimilar from our sun, so that at least one of their planets might be similar to the earth? Second, is there any reason to believe that the kind of primeval organisms from which life eventually evolved on earth exist elsewhere in the cosmos?

The first of these questions can be answered with some degree of certainty. The earth is about 4,000 million years old and the palaeontologists tell us that some forms of life have existed for the last thousand million years. Thus the atoms of the initial pre-biotic material have evolved into intelligent life in a period of not less than a thousand million and not more than 4,000 million years. There are various biological arguments which lead to the conclusion that even under radically different conditions of radiation and environment this long-drawn-out period of evolution is unlikely to be capable of much shortening if some form of intelligent being is to evolve. Extraterrestrial life of the type in which we are interested therefore requires a planet to be situated near a star which can maintain suitable conditions over at least a period of say 3,000 million years.

Astronomers have been able to classify stars into a number of distinct types indicative of such features as their mass, luminosity, and their evolutionary state. Some of these stellar types may be dismissed immediately from the present consideration because the time they spend in a stable configuration, where the energy output is exactly balanced by the thermonuclear reactions in the core of the star, is only ten million to a hundred million years. Even if organic evolution began on planets belonging to such a star it would certainly perish when the output of heat and light from the star began to change. At the other end of the scale there are types of star which can anticipate stable conditions for at least a hundred thousand million years. These are of low luminosity and the chance that a planet of such a star lies at a distance from it which ensures the temperate conditions necessary for the evolution of life is rather small. In between these extremes there exists a range of stellar types with stable life times of several thousands of millions of years, and with sufficient luminosity to give reasonable chances that a planet will move in a habitable zone. The sun is typical of a star in this class.

There is one further reason for excluding many stars of whatever type from consideration. We know that at least one-half of the stars in the solar neighbourhood are not single, individual stars, like the sun, but are binaries, or multiples in which two or more stars revolve around one another. Unless the separation of the stars in a binary or multiple system is very large it is unlikely that a planet can be in a sufficiently stable orbit around one of the stars.

The net result of these considerations is that probably only a few per cent. of all stars are in a condition where one of their planets is able to sustain some form of organic evolution. In the solar neighbourhood, where our detailed knowledge of stars is greatest, the number in this category has been estimated to be about five per cent. In order to obtain a probable lower estimate of the numbers involved in the Milky Way, we will reduce this figure to one per cent. Since there are about one hundred thousand million stars in the Milky Way system this means that some thousand million stars must have planets in the appropriate condition to support long-term organic evolution.

It may be argued that the fivefold reduction which we have already made in the original estimate is an insufficient margin of error. Suppose then that we make the extremely unlikely assumption that the original estimate is not 5 but 5,000 times wrong. In this case we conclude that there must be still a hundred million stars in the Milky Way with planets which could support organic evolution.

When we consider the wider aspects of the cosmos as a whole the situation becomes even more dramatic. The structure of the Milky Way system of stars, of which the sun is a member, is typical in size and form of the spiral nebulae which are known to populate extragalactic space as far as our telescopes penetrate. The 200-inch telescope on Mount Palomar can photograph clusters of galaxies at distances of a few thousand million light years. Within this observable part of the universe there must be at least a thousand million galaxies with a size, structure, and stellar content not dissimilar from that of our local galaxy or Milky Way system. Our estimates therefore lead us to conclude that in the observable universe there are probably some trillion stars possessing planets in a suitable condition for the support of organic evolution.

We then come to the second question as to whether the earth itself has any uniquely favourable conditions among these trillions of planets which enable life to arise on its surface. This issue has, of course, been engulfed in philosophical and religious doctrines for centuries. Today, however, both the scientist and the theologian from their different standpoints treat the situation in a realistic manner. The basic chemical bricks of life, particularly hydrogen and carbon, are plentiful throughout the universe, but until the last few decades the majority of scientists have been convinced that under natural conditions the hydrocarbons and their derivatives could arise only by biogenesis, that is through the agency of living beings. Now the position has changed in a radical manner and many routes for the inanimate synthesis of complex organic molecules are understood.

Indeed, the position regarding the existence of complex organic molecules outside the earth has been removed from the realms of speculation during the last two or three years by the

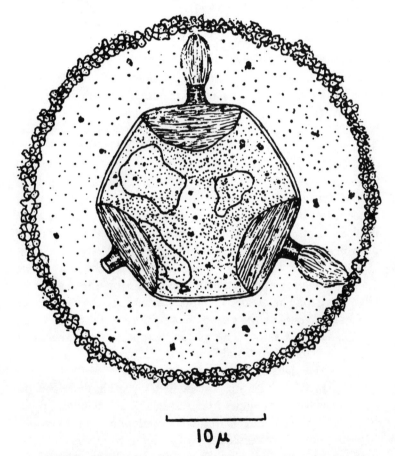

10 μ

Fig. 8. Sketch of organized element consisting of a structureless halo and three vacuole-like irregular-shaped bodies in the interior. Such an organized element was found on the Orgueil meteorite. This may well represent the remnant of an organism of extraterrestrial origin. (*By kind permission of Professor Nagy and the editors of* Nature)

work of Calvin and Vaughn and other American scientists on the organic analysis of fallen meteorites. These analyses have revealed the presence on the meteoritic material of hydrocarbons and complex organic molecules, including structures similar to cytosine, which is one of the bases of nucleic acid. It is, therefore, no longer realistic to question the possibility that the complex molecules of living beings can arise through abiotic processes.

THE BURDEN OF PROOF

Although the answers to the fundamental questions are favourable as regards the widespread occurrence of life in the universe, there are serious gaps remaining in the chain of argument. At the moment the main gaps appear in the sequence of biological reasoning, and here the most serious concerns the formation of replicating polymers. The substance of the above discussion is that organic compounds will arise abiotically and will accumulate in the primeval oceans or elsewhere until their rate of formation reaches equilibrium with thermal or other processes of decomposition. However, the actual formation of replicating polymers in such a morass leading to the appearance of voracious organisms has not yet been realized experimentally. One of the most significant features of modern technology is that we can visualize observational approaches on the cosmos to close this gap. The biological approach concerns the use of space probes to investigate the existence of primitive organisms within the planetary system. The physical approach envisages the actual possibility of establishing communication with communities elsewhere in the cosmos.

The American biologist Joshua Lederberg has described the equipment which he hopes to install in a future planetary probe to investigate the state of organic development of Mars and Venus. This consists essentially of a microscope with an automatic collecting device which would feed in samples of the planetary atmospheres or surfaces. A travelling ribbon of transparent tape would slowly carry the samples past the aperture of the microscope. The resultant pictures would be transmitted back to earth by techniques which are familiar and have, indeed, already been demonstrated in practice by the Russians in their transmissions of the Lunik III pictures of the moon. Although the device is relatively unsophisticated there is every reason to anticipate that it will possess the ability to convey to the earth clear indications of the existence of any organisms on these planets. One need only imagine the situation in reverse to envisage the abundant evidence of life on earth which could be conveyed by the similar microscopic inspection of a grain of dust or drop of water. The discovery of developing organisms, however primitive, on the planetary surfaces or in their atmosphere would add a new and vital factor of certainty to the concept of extraterrestrial existence.

The physical approach of establishing interstellar communication was first seriously suggested on the basis of available techniques by Cocconi and Morrison of New York, and a preliminary experiment was subsequently carried out by Drake using a radio telescope at the National Radio Observatory in America. The idea is based on the concept that if communities exist on any of the planetary systems associated with the stars in the galaxy, then at least some will be technologically in advance of ourselves. They will have known perhaps for hundreds or thousands of years the facts which are only just being revealed to ourselves. They will have appreciated that the most likely chance of establishing interstellar communication is through the use of giant radio telescopes, transmitting and receiving signals in the radio part of the electromagnetic spectrum. Since the scrutiny of the entire radio spectrum for a weak interstellar signal may well appal even an advanced community, they will have sought for a unique standard of frequency which would be known to every observer in the universe. It happens that just such a standard of radio emission exists in the universe—the emission generated on a wavelength of 21 cm. in the neutral hyrdogen gas which pervades the galaxies of the cosmos. It is, therefore, reasonable to expect that an advanced interstellar community would endeavour to establish contact with us by transmitting signals in this frequency band. Cocconi and Morrison calculated that with the larger radio telescopes now available on earth and with the assumption of similar equipment and reasonable transmitting powers in the advanced communites, it should be possible for observers situated in stellar systems up to 10 to 20 light years distant from the sun to communicate with the earth.

This was basically the argument with which Cocconi and Morrison endeavoured to persuade me to use the Jodrell Bank telescope in the search for intelligible extraterrestrial signals.

THE ETHICAL STATE OF CIVILIZATIONS

Although the burden of the final proof remains, the state of our present fundamental knowledge favours the view that life exists or has at least developed in many parts of the cosmos. Disregarding the possibility of exotic forms of development under conditions dissimilar from our own environment, it is also reasonable to assume that development of such communities will have followed the same pattern as the development of life on earth.

Through a period of the order of a thousand million years life will have developed from the primeval material, and at some stage in this development the kind of state which we now find on earth may have been reached. In view of the time scale which is now set for the evolution of the universe it is conceivable that some of these communities will have reached this stage of development in an age which is long past as far as we on earth are concerned.

At this point they will, like us, have reached a supremely critical state of development in which the sudden breakthrough of science and technology has produced vast material powers, including possibilities of self-destruction, before the community as a whole has had time or opportunity to adjust itself to their proper use for the advantage of the species.

The number of communities likely to be involved is so great and the balance is so delicate at this stage of development that many communities have perhaps perished. Those which have survived the crisis will possess a technological and scientific potential which is very hard for us to envisage on earth. Indeed, an extrapolation of our own accelerated technical development over the last fifty years to hundreds or thousands of years would produce facilities which it is not possible for us to imagine.

The crisis in a civilization is likely to be short-lived. After slow and often painfully protracted development through millions of years of evolution intelligent beings will quite suddenly face an entirely new ethical situation—at least in magnitude if not in principle. Our civilization has reached this stage during the last twenty years, and the basic reason is simple to describe but profoundly hard to remedy.

Science in some form or other has existed for more than a thousand years but only in the last few hundred years has science become a sequential activity as distinct from a sporadic semi-philosophical occupation. During the last fifty or a hundred years organizations of diverse interest—military and commercial— have appreciated that these investigations of nature can be profitable for their own ends although their primary purpose may be to increase man's fundamental knowledge of himself and his environment.

This appreciation is not in itself necessarily dangerous but, in fact, the actual result is that science has been professionalized to such an extent that over 90 per cent. of the scientists who have ever lived are alive and at work today. Almost within a few decades there has been an avalanche of scientific and technical discovery and development without parallel in history. Individual man and his collective organizations have meanwhile continued in their slow and non-sequential forms of development in all the aspects of activity which control the development of this wealth of science and technology.

Forty years ago Schweitzer, in his *Civilization and Ethics*, considered the problem of why in the sphere of ethics we live in a town full of ruins, in which one generation builds for itself here, and another there, what is absolutely necessary. Then the dichotomy was of relatively minor significance, in that the con-sequential failings of man involved human suffering and death individually and sometimes nationally. Now we have moved to a new horizon where the entire fate of another of the civilizations of the cosmos is at stake.

The common evidence of this is, of course, the imminent fear of conflict involving atomic weapons. Arguments that man would today survive such an eruption are irrelevant to this discussion. Whether or not the arguments are correct now, it is axiomatic that they will become incorrect within a further decade or so of technology in its present precipitous state of activity.

However, the hydrogen bomb, although the most obvious and imminent source of man's concern, is neither the sole nor necessarily the most cosmically significant illustration of our ethical peril. At least of equal import are some of the projected space activities of man which may result in the contamination of the extraterrestrial environment. The newly acquired technical ability of human beings to launch satellites, space probes, and space ships involves hazards where the judgement between right and wrong is thinly veiled. Throughout the centuries the judgement between right and wrong in the use of explosives, for example, has become defined. It is justifiable to use explosive force for quarrying but it is wrong to use the same explosive in an attack on another human being. It is permitted to unlock the tremendous power in the atomic nucleus for the generation of energy but if the nations release this power in the form of a bomb then the existence of all peoples is in jeopardy. In the same way few would deny that the use of the rocket designed to carry such a bomb would be quite justified when used to carry a satellite, space probe, or a man into space.

Today a new peril has arisen in an activity only a few years old, involving ethical judgements of extraterrestrial problems. On what basis do national groups assess their right to contaminate extraterrestrial space and the planets of the solar system with objects constructed and launched from earth? Few would cavil at the assumed right to place in orbit around the earth satellites and probes used for scientific investigation which eventually return and burn up in the earth's atmosphere. An entirely different situation arises if the satellite or probe is used principally to establish national prestige, or for commercial or military purposes in a manner prejudicial to other global or extraterrestrial interests. The difficulty of judgement is well illustrated by the proposal to use space vehicles for purposes of world communication. The launching of the Echo balloon satellite for the testing of long-distance communication via space endangers no other global interests and requires no international justification. The other American proposal, to place many hundreds of millions of thin wires into orbit around the earth for a communication system (Project Needles or West Ford), may eventually be prejudicial to other interests, and the contamination of space to this extent for national interests is ethically wrong.

In the exploration of the moon and the planets with space vehicles we are faced with problems of far greater gravity. The moon rockets launched by the Soviet Union in the autumn of 1959 were brilliant exploits and rightly excited the admiration of people everywhere. Lunik III was launched in an orbit around the moon and transmitted photographs of the hidden side to earth—an entirely justifiable and wonderfully executed scientific feat. However, a few weeks earlier Lunik II was directed at the moon and crashed on the lunar surface during the evening of 13 September. In this kind of activity the problem of cosmic ethics begins to arise in an acute form. Fortunately in the case of Lunik II the lunar impact of an earth rocket is unlikely to disturb the subsequent investigations of the moon which, because of the aridity of the moon, will almost certainly be physical in character and not biological.

The problem arises predominantly with the space probes which will be launched towards Venus and Mars by America and the Soviet Union. Already, both nations have attempted to reach the vicinity of Venus by rockets launched from earth, but the space capsules have passed thousands of miles from the planet. This situation will change and soon the probe launched to penetrate the atmosphere of the planet or land on its surface will succeed in its mission. Our knowledge of the biological situation on Mars and Venus is fragmentary in the extreme and, in the case of Venus, man has not yet been able to see the surface of the planet. The outstanding significance of the biological investigations has already been emphasized, and every principle of science and ethics will be disregarded if either the Soviet Union or

America proceeds with these investigations of the planets in any way which will prejudice this work.

The impact of a terrestrial rocket on Mars or Venus, in the manner of Lunik II on the moon, would certainly be an un-mitigated scientific and moral disaster: a scientific disaster because the rocket could carry to the planet earthly organisms and thereby severely handicap future biological work, and a moral disaster because man will have presumed the right to inject his own contaminated material into an extraterrestrial environment where organic evolution may well be in progress. This is not an argument for suspending the investigation of the planets by space probes. On the contrary, every possible influence and priority should be given to these investigations to ensure that the first approaches to the planets are made at a distance with probes carrying instruments which can first assess the biological situa-tion. If any national group disregards this scientific and ethical principle for chauvinistic reasons then the decay of our civilization will assume extraterrestrial as well as global attributes. The extraterrestrial environment may indeed be inanimate but it is folly on a cosmic scale for man to assume that it is so without first obtaining proof by all the means now at his disposal.

THE BASIS FOR OPTIMISM

The optimism engendered by the tremendous accomplish-ments of man in science and all forms of creative activity is constantly diminished by the failure of national groups to apply appropriate ethical standards to the power at their disposal. There is scarcely a major scientific advance of the century which does not carry with it the powers of good or evil, and in every generation there are the voices which, in the face of the ever-recurring crises, will either assume an attitude of passive pessimism or will seek to dam up the outlets of man's insatiable curiosity.

It is hard to believe that these attitudes are in any sense constructive since they aim to suspend the development of world civilization in the moment of crisis. On the contrary, it seems likely that civilizations which survive are those where the challenge of scientific and technical progress is accepted, thus providing the driving force enabling the community to pass rapidly through the years of crisis without self-extermination.

Today there are grounds for the belief that these processes are rapidly emerging on earth. Only a few years ago the global scene appeared to be profoundly bleak, with the vast resources of two great nations devoted to the establishment of a parity of long-range ballistic rockets mounting atomic warheads. The fundamental breakthrough of this barrier came when Russia used one of those rockets for purposes other than destruction—the launching of Sputnik I in October 1957. In the succeeding years the main contestants have poured more and more of their resources into these new triumphs of science and technology. The announcement, in the spring of 1961 by the President, that the United States was to engage in a vast programme designed to place an American on the moon before a Russian, may indeed be recognized in history as one of the fundamental turning points in the world crisis. In order to accomplish this feat a significant fraction of the nation's science and technology will be diverted to an achievement which, in itself, has no direct military significance but which will nevertheless use some 10 per cent. of the resources which might otherwise find a military outlet on earth. In the Soviet Union it is clear that the determination exists and the diversion from the direct military machine must be similar. Within two or three decades, when the planets, not the moon, become the targets, the expenditure and effort will be so colossal that it will be hard for the nations to sustain the global military machines in a developing state.

Man's interest and resources seem likely to pass rapidly to this extraterrestrial environment during the next two decades. In this process the global dangers will probably subside but the peoples of the earth must exercise the utmost restraint and vigilance as the major ethical dilemma which now pervades us assumes cosmical attributes.

APPENDIX

In Chapter V a letter from an American scientist is mentioned. Jodrell Bank receives its share of correspondence based on fantasy from unknown authors. This letter was different: a suggestion which seemed fantastic, but originating from a scientist of distinction who had produced straightforward calculations which could not be lightly dismissed. It is reproduced here by the kind consent of its author, because of its inherent interest and because it must be one of the first of the scientific documents about radio communication with extraterrestrial beings. Our descendants will surely be interested in this correspondence of the mid-twentieth century. They will know either that we were inept in engaging in such idle speculation—or that we were so lacking in initiative that we failed to make one of the greatest discoveries of all time.

CERN European Organisation for Nuclear Research.
Meyrin—Geneva   29th June, 1959.

Dear Dr. Lovell,

My name is probably unknown to you, so let me start by saying that I am now at CERN for one year, on leave from Cornell University, where I am professor of Physics.

Some weeks ago, while discussing with colleagues at Cornell the emission of synchrotron radiation by astronomical objects, I realized that the Jodrell Bank radio telescope could be used for a program that could be serious enough to deserve your consideration, though at first sight it looks like science fiction.

It will be better if I itemize the arguments.

(1) Life on planets seems not to be a very rare phenomenon. Out of ten solar planets one is full of life and Mars could have some. The solar system is not peculiar; other stars with similar characteristics are expected to have an equivalent number of planets. There is a good chance that, among the, say, 100 stars closest to the sun, some have planets bearing life well advanced in evolution.

82

(2) The chances are then good that in some of these planets animals exist evolved much farther than men. A civilization only a few hundred years more advanced than ours would have technical possibilities by far greater than those available now to us.

(3) Assume that an advanced civilization exists in some of these planets, i.e. within some 10 light years from us. The problem is: how to establish a communication?

As far as we know the only possibility seems to be the use of electromagnetic waves, which can cross the magnetized plasmas filling the interstellar spaces without being distorted.

So I will assume that 'beings' on these planets are already sending toward the stars closest to them beams of electromagnetic waves modulated in a rational way, e.g. in trains corresponding to the prime-numbers, hoping in a sign of life.

(4) The planets, as seen from another star, are all within one second of arc from their sun and cannot be easily resolved. To make it detectable, the emission from a planet must then be greater than that of the star itself. This limits the useful radiation to the radio waves and to the ultra gammas. The first seems more promising from the point of view of both the emission and the detection.

(5) If 'they' use a mirror similar to that of Jodrell Bank and if their sun emits as our quiet sun does, the emitted power must be larger than some 10^{-5} watts $(c/s)^{-1}$ at $f = 10^9$ c/s, a modest requirement.

(6) However such a source could not be detected by us. It would be swamped by the galactic background.

On the average this background is—

$$\frac{dW_b}{dS \; d\Omega \; df} = 10^{-12 \cdot 7} f^{-1} \quad \text{watts} \quad \text{m}^{-2} \quad \text{steradian}^{-1} \quad (c/s)^{-1}$$

If the detector is a mirror of diameter l_d, i.e., with opening angle $\theta_d = \dfrac{\lambda}{l_d}$ then the background on the detector is

$$\frac{dW_b}{dS \; df} = \frac{dW_b}{dS \; d\Omega \; df} \; \theta^2_d = \frac{10^{4 \cdot 3}}{f^3 \; l^2_d} \quad \text{watts} \quad \text{m}^{-2} \quad (c/s)^{-1} \quad (l \text{ in metres})$$

If the source is at a distance r from the Earth, in order to be distinguishable it has to supply a power W_s such that

$$\frac{dW_s}{df} \cdot \frac{G_s}{4\pi r^2} > \frac{dW_q}{dS \; df},$$

where $\quad G_s = \dfrac{4\pi}{\theta^2_s} = \dfrac{4\pi}{(\lambda/l_s)^2}\quad$ is the gain of the source mirror.

Hence $\quad \dfrac{dW_s}{df} > \dfrac{10^{21.3}\ r^2}{f^5\ l^2_s\ l^2_d}\quad$ watts $(c/s)^{-1}$

Assuming that both the source and the detector consist of a Jodrell Bank mirror, $r = 10$ light years $= 10^{17}$m, and $f = 10^9$c/s,

$\dfrac{dW_s}{df} > 10^{2.7}$ watts $(c/s)^{-1}$, a difficult task for us. But I want to have faith and will assume that they have larger mirrors and more powerful emitters and can do it.

(7) What I propose is thus a systematic survey of the stars closest to us and spectroscopically similar to the sun, looking for man-made signals.

As I said before, all this is most probably fiction, but it would be most interesting if it were not.

I leave to you the judgement on the feasibility of such a search.

My best regards,

Sincerely yours,

G. Cocconi

INDEX

Ambartsumian, V. A., 48, 56
Andromeda, nebula in, 3, 10, 11, 36, 43, 44, 47, 51, 52, 55
Arizona meteorite, 28
asteroids, 18
astronomy, optical, 1–4, 35; radio, *see* radio astronomy
atmosphere and radiations, 4
Aurora borealis and van Allen belts, 22–23

Baade, W., 42, 47, 55
blue stars, 47, 48
Bondi, Hermann, 61
Boötes, galaxies in, 54, 60, 61, 63

Calvin, M., 74
Capella, 7, 38
Cassiopeia, 42, 55
Ceres, 18
civilization, ethical state of, 76
Cocconi, G., on extraterrestrial life, 75, 76
Coma galaxies, 53
Comets, 25
communication via space vehicles, 78, 79
cosmic rays, origin of, 23
cosmology in relation to philosophy and theology, 66–67
cosmos, ethical considerations, 68–81; theories of, 61–63
Crab nebula, 41, 42, 50
crisis in civilization, 76, 77, 81
Cygnus, colliding galaxies in, 55–56; nebula in, 42

doppler effect, 46, 53

earth, age of, 33, 70; origin of life on, 70, 72
earth satellites, 11–16; importance of, 12; measuring micrometeorites, 27, 28

Eddington, Sir Arthur, 67; theory of universe, 65
Einstein, A., 61
ethics and the cosmos, 68–81
evolutionary theory of universe, 62, 63–67
Explorer satellites, 13, 23
extragalactic nebulae, radio emission, 43

galaxies, arrangement of stars in, 35–37; collision of, 60, 61; distribution of, 58–59; magnetic fields around, 11; nuclei of, 46–47, 50; recession of, 53–54; shapes of, 37; spatial density of, 62, 63; spiral formation of, 46; velocities of, 53–54
Galileo, 3, 20
Gamov, G., theory of universe, 64
Giacobini–Zinner comet, 25
Gold, T., 61

Herschel, W., 2
Hoyle, F., 61
Hubble, E. P., 3, 53
Hydrogen gas: as origin of radio waves, 8; formation of, 48; in galactic nucleus, 47; radio emission from, 38, 44–48; star formation from, 48–51; 21 cm. radio emission from, 45, 46, 75
hydrogen-helium conversion, 49

interplanetary dust, 27; around the earth, 28; origin of, 29
interplanetary space, 19–20
interstellar communication, 75, 82–84
interstellar gas, 35–36; magnetic fields in, 22

Jansky, Karl, first detects radiation from space, 5, 8
Jodrell Bank telescope, 12, 59; description of, 8–10

85